CAUTION CREEK FORMATION		SURPRISE CREEK FORMATION			
2	1	7 6 5	4	3	2

SURPRISE CREEK

A small tributary of Churchill River. Members of Surprise Creek and Caution Creek formations indicated by numbers (see text).

The Geological Society of America
Memoir 90

ORDOVICIAN PALEONTOLOGY OF THE NORTHERN HUDSON BAY LOWLAND

By

SAMUEL J. NELSON

University of Alberta
Calgary, Alberta, Canada

1963

TEXT COMPOSED AND PRINTED BY WAVERLY PRESS, INC.
COLLOTYPE PLATES BY MERIDEN GRAVURE CO.
BINDING BY RUSSELL-RUTTER CO.

Address all communications to The Geological Society of America
New York, N. Y.

The Memoir Series
of
The Geological Society of America
is made possible
through the bequest of
Richard Alexander Fullerton Penrose, Jr.

ACKNOWLEDGMENTS

The late Prof. A. K. Miller of the State University of Iowa, Profs. E. C. Stumm of the University of Michigan, C. R. Stelck, P. S. Warren, and E. May of the University of Alberta, V. J. Okulitch of the University of British Columbia, T. H. Clark of McGill University, Walter Youngquist of the University of Oregon, and Dr. Curt Teichert of the United States Geological Survey have given generously of their time in helping the writer prepare this report. Officers of the Geological Survey of Canada have also extended much help and guidance.

Residents of the northern Lowland who have helped, and extended hospitality, are almost too numerous to mention. In particular the writer wishes to express his thanks to Mr. and Mrs. John Kinaschuk, formerly of mile 352, Hudson Bay Railway.

The writer extends his gratitude to his wife Marjorie who has helped throughout most of this study, and to Miss S. Baker and Miss E. Dingman for their stenographic assistance.

A sincere expression of thanks is due the writer's field assistants for their enthusiastic co-operation: R. Procter, J. Wishart, L. Keating, D. Walker, and G. Goodwin.

Generous financial assistance has been provided the writer by grants from the National Research Council of Canada and the University of Alberta.

CONTENTS

ILLUSTRATIONS

PLATES

FIGURES

TABLE

ABSTRACT

The Late Ordovician fauna of the northern Hudson Bay Lowland, Manitoba, Canada, consisting of three stromatoporoid species (1 new), 41 coral (11 new and 2 new genera), 8 gastropod (1 new), 56 cephalopod (21 new and 1 new genus), and 1 graptolite species are described and in part illustrated. Brachiopods are listed only. This fauna was obtained from five formations consisting mostly of fossiliferous dolomitic limestone 300–400 feet thick. In ascending order these are: the Portage Chute and Surprise Creek formations of the Bad Cache Rapids Group; the Caution Creek and Chasm Creek formations of the Churchill River Group; and the Red Head Rapids Formation. The Bad Cache Rapids Group, which rests on peneplaned Precambrian, is correlated with the Red River Formation of southern Manitoba, the Churchill River Group with the Stony Mountain Formation, and the Red Head Rapids Formation questionably with the Stonewall Formation.

The faunas indicate a close temporal relationship between the Bad Cache Rapids and Churchill River groups. The latter is considered Richmondian and in part Gamachian. A Late Ordovician age is thus also suggested for the Bad Cache Rapids Group and hence for the coeval Red River Formation.

1

INTRODUCTION

GENERAL STATEMENT

During the field seasons of 1950 and 1951 the writer examined the Ordovician and Silurian rocks of the northern Hudson Bay Lowland. The work was done under the auspices of the Geological Survey of Canada, and a report on the stratigraphy of this area (Nelson, 1964) has been prepared for the Survey. The present report is concerned primarily with the description of Ordovician fossils collected on Nelson, Churchill, South Knife, and North Knife rivers (Fig. 1). Conclusions regarding age relationships and correlation are the responsibility of the author alone.

Because the northern Lowland is swampy, outcrops are rare except along major rivers. Of the four traversed, Churchill River has the most nearly complete Ordovician succession and probably one of the best sections in the Hudson Bay Lowland. Silurian outcrops have been found only on Nelson River and along the coast from Port Churchill to the Cape Churchill area.

PREVIOUS WORK

Reports dealing with parts of the area studied have been presented by Bell (1879; 1880), McInnes (1913), Parks (1915; *in* Tyrrell, 1913), Alcock (1916), Savage and Van Tuyl (1919), Miller and Youngquist (1947b), Williams (1948), and Ethington and Furnish (1959).

The geology of the Nelson River has been described by Bell, and that of the Churchill by both Bell and Alcock. McInnes summarized Bell's work but added no new data. In 1912, Tyrrell, during a boundary survey for the Province of Ontario, collected fossils from the region south of the area under study, and some specimens from drift near the mouth of Nelson River. Later, Parks (1915; *in* Tyrrell, 1913) studied and described Tyrrell's collections.

The first systematic investigation of the Hudson Bay Ordovician was undertaken by Savage and Van Tuyl (1919); their studies were confined to the Nelson River and the area to the south. Two Ordovician formations were recognized: the Nelson River Formation with its type area along the Nelson, and the younger Shamattawa Formation with its type area along Gods River.

Savage and Van Tuyl designated the Ordovician succession along Nelson River by numbers. "Units" 1–4 constituted the Nelson River Formation, 68 feet of dolomite and limestone on a basal sandstone. The formation was considered Middle Ordovician and correlated with the strata in southern Manitoba now called Red River Formation. "Units" 5–7 were placed in the Shamattawa Formation which, along the Nelson, was described as consisting of about 47 feet of limestone. The formation was equated with the Richmondian Stony Mountain Formation of southern Manitoba.

For 28 years after Savage and Van Tuyl's work no new data were published on the northern Lowland. Miller and Youngquist (1947b) described Ordovician fossils collected in the vicinity of Port Churchill and from along the North Knife River.

3

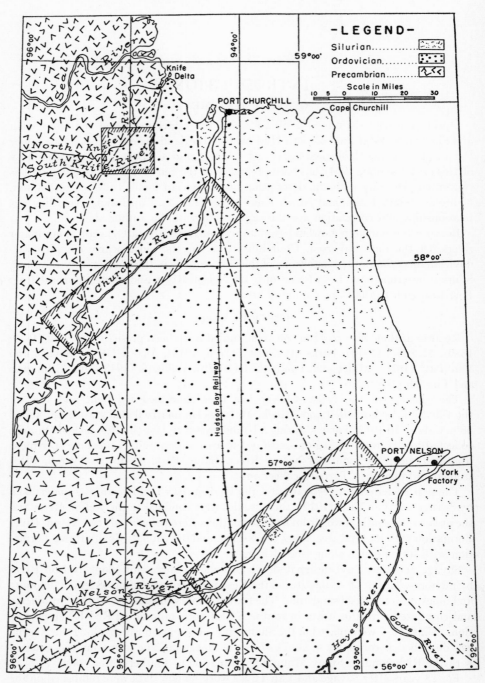

FIGURE 1. Geological sketch map of northern Hudson Bay Lowland. Insets refer to areas covered by Figures 3 and 4.

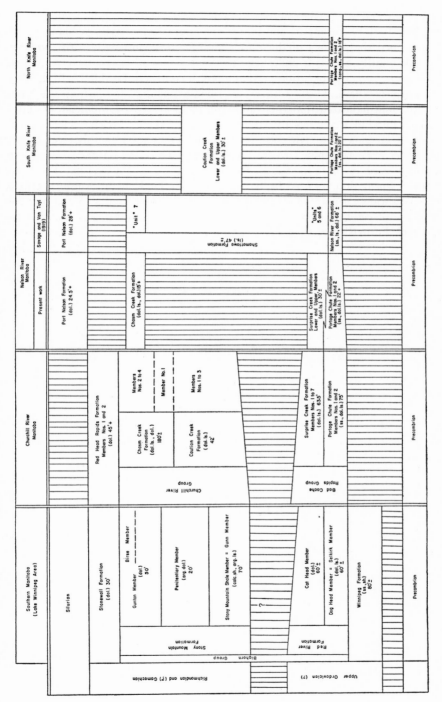

FIGURE 2. Correlation chart of Ordovician formations of northern Hudson Bay Lowland

Although they did not visit this river, they suggested that Ordovician may be present along both its lower part and that of the South Knife River. Williams (1948) briefly described the geology of the Port Churchill area, noted that drift boulders were predominantly Silurian, and suggested that strata of that age were present there. The most recent publication pertaining to the northern Lowland is by Ething-ton and Furnish (1959). These workers described a conodont fauna from the Knife Delta region and indicated that the containing rocks are Late Ordovician in age.

Because Churchill River has the best exposures of the Ordovician succession in the northern Hudson Bay Lowland, formational names used on this river by the present writer are also applied to the other rivers. Thus the term Portage Chute Formation is used in place of Nelson River Formation on the Nelson. The name Shamattawa Formation, as used by Savage and Van Tuyl on the Nelson, actually embraces two widely separated stratigraphic horizons. Their "units" 5 and 6 of this formation are placed in the Surprise Creek Formation, and "unit" 7 is placed in the Chasm Creek Formation of this report (Fig. 2).

STRATIGRAPHY

GENERAL STATEMENT

Ordovician strata of the northern Hudson Bay Lowland are predominantly dolomitic limestone. On Churchill River they have a maximum thickness of 300–400 feet. Most strata dip gently eastward and extend north-northwest as a broad belt, about 50 miles wide, from Nelson to Churchill River. The belt narrows north of the Churchill and disappears in the Knife Delta region (Fig. 1). The boundary with the Silurian is approximate and is based mainly on drift.

Five Ordovician formations are recognized (in ascending order): the Portage Chute and Surprise Creek formations of the Bad Cache Rapids Group, Caution Creek and Chasm Creek formations of the Churchill River Group, and the Red Head Rapids Formation (Fig. 2).

The Bad Cache Rapids Group rests on peneplaned Precambrian and is as much as 140 feet thick. It is correlated with the Red River Formation of southern Manitoba. The Churchill River Group rests paraconformably on the Bad Cache Rapids Group. The former is probably about 180 feet thick and is correlated with the Stony Mountain Formation. The Red Head Rapids Formation is probably about 40 feet thick and is questionably correlated with the Stonewall Formation of southern Manitoba.

Silurian strata, not described in this report, crop out along the coast, as well as along Nelson River, where they extend over a small area about 11 miles downstream from Lower Limestone Rapids. These outcrops constitute the type section of Savage and Van Tuyl's (1919) Port Nelson Formation and consist of about 25 feet of dolomite. Ordovician strata occur both up- and down-river from this section, but contacts have not been observed. The Port Nelson is interpreted as a small synclinal outlier superjacent to the Ordovician.

BAD CACHE RAPIDS GROUP

GENERAL STATEMENT

On Churchill River the Bad Cache Rapids Group is nearly continuously exposed for about 19 miles, from near Portage Chute to the mouth of Surprise Creek. The group has also been recognized through scattered outcrops on Nelson, South Knife, and North Knife rivers.

The Portage Chute Formation correlates with the Dog Head Member of the Red River Formation, and the Surprise Creek probably with the Cat Head. The Bad Cache Rapids Group is considered Upper Ordovician and equivalent to some part of the Eden, Maysville, and lower Richmond strata.

PORTAGE CHUTE FORMATION

The Portage Chute Formation is well exposed on Churchill River from Portage Chute to Bad Cache Rapids (Fig. 3; Pl. 2, fig. 1). Over this 13-mile stretch outcrops are nearly continuous, and many form near-vertical cliffs 25–75 feet high. Below Bad Cache Rapids the formation is generally exposed in low, rather rubbly outcrops. Although the unit is named for the locality of Portage Chute, the type section

7

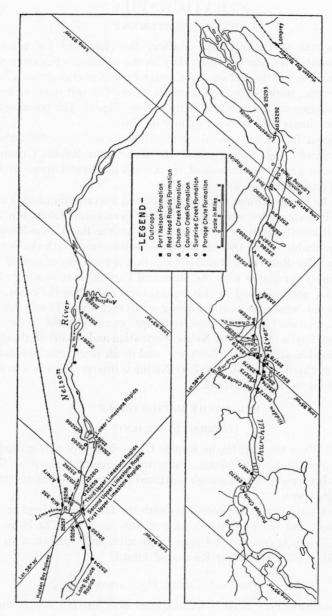

FIGURE 3. Map of Nelson and Churchill rivers showing fossil localities and principal Ordovician outcrop areas

is designated at the more accessible locality 25272 on the south side of Bad Cache Rapids. Here both lower and upper contacts of the formation are well exposed.

The formation is 75 feet thick; the basal 4 feet are referred to Member No. 1 and the remaining part to Member No. 2. Member No. 1 consists of a fairly uniform calcareous quartz sandstone resting on peneplaned Precambrian granitic rock. Except for fucoidal impressions the only fossils known from the member are rare *Charactocerina kirki* Foerste and *Maclurites manitobensis* (Whiteaves).

Member No. 2, 71 feet thick, is transitionally conformable with the underlying unit and is gray- to buff-weathering, light-gray, microcrystalline, slightly dolomitic limestone in beds 1 inch to 2 feet thick. Fragmental organic material is common. Closely spaced, rusty-weathering, anastomosing laminae within the limestone are characteristic and in many places give the member a nodular appearance upon weathering.

Member No. 2 is richly fossiliferous; because of its cliff-forming habit many collections were made from rubble at the bottom. Its fauna consists predominantly of corals, gastropods, and cephalopods. The following species have been identified:

Incertae sedis
 Receptaculites sp.

Corals
 Palaeophyllum stokesi (Milne-Edwards and Haime)
 P. halysitoides (Wilson)
 Grewingkia robusta (Whiteaves)
 Favistella alveolata (Goldfuss)
 Saffordophyllum(?) *portagechutense* sp. nov.
 Calapoecia anticostiensis Billings
 Plasmopora lambei Schuchert
 P. pattersoni Roy
 Catenipora rubra Sinclair and Bolton
 C. robusta (Wilson)
 C. stearni sp. nov.
 C. aequabilis (Teichert)
 C. agglomeratiformis (Whitfield)
 Manipora amicarum Sinclair
 M. irregularis (Teichert)
 M. feildeni (Etheridge)

Brachiopods
 Diceromyonia sp.
 Thaerodonta sp.
 Strophomena spp.

Gastropods
 Trochonema coxi Wilson
 Holopea gigantea sp. nov.

Hormotoma winnipegensis Whiteaves
Maclurites manitobensis (Whiteaves)
M. altus Wilson
M. ungava Wilson
Fusispira gigantea Wilson

Cephalopods
 Narthecoceras crassisiphonatum (Whiteaves)
 Lambeoceras landerense Foerste
 L. baffinense Miller, Youngquist, and Collinson
 Paractinoceras canadense (Whiteaves)
 Whiteavesites winnipegensis (Whiteaves)
 Billingsites costulatus (Whiteaves)
 B. landerensis Foerste
 Digenuoceras latum (Foerste)
 Exomegoceras wyomingense Miller and Carrier
 Neumatoceras churchillense sp. nov.
 Westonoceras nelsonense Foerste
 Winnipegoceras laticurvatum (Whiteaves)
 Cyrtogomphoceras turgidum Troedsson(?)
 C. nutatum Foerste and Savage
 C. baffinense Foerste
 C. thompsoni Miller and Furnish
 C. alcocki sp. nov.
 Charactoceras manitobense sp. nov.
 Wilsonoceras squawcreekense Miller

On the Nelson River the Portage Chute Formation crops out from near Long Spruce Rapids to a short distance below the Third Upper Limestone Rapids (Fig. 3; Pl. 3, fig. 1). Throughout this distance of about 8 miles, exposures are generally low and scattered and make estimates of total thickness uncertain. Both members are present and are lithologically identical with corresponding units on Churchill River. Member No. 1 is 4 feet thick. The minimum thickness of Member No. 2 is 21 feet; the maximum is probably not much more.

Except for vague traces of fucoids Member No. 1 is barren. Member No. 2, however, is fairly fossiliferous, and the following fauna has been identified:

Incertae sedis
Receptaculites sp.

Corals
Palaeophyllum halysitoides (Wilson)
Grewingkia robusta (Whiteaves)
Saffordophyllum(?) portagechutense sp. nov.
Plasmopora lambei Schuchert
P. pattersoni Roy
Catenipora rubra Sinclair and Bolton
C. robusta (Wilson)
C. stearni sp. nov.
Manipora amicarum Sinclair
M. irregularis (Teichert)
M. feildeni (Etheridge)

Gastropods
Trochonema coxi Wilson
Hormotoma winnipegensis Whiteaves

Maclurites manitobensis (Whiteaves)
M. altus Wilson
Fusispira gigantea Wilson

Cephalopods
?Cyclendoceras kindlei Foerste
Narthecoceras crassisiphonatum (Whiteaves)
Billingsites costulatus (Whiteaves)
Westonoceras nelsonense Foerste and Savage
Winnipegoceras laticurvatum (Whiteaves)
W. dowlingi Foerste
W. nelsonense sp. nov.
Cyrtogomphoceras turgidum Troedsson
C. nutatum Foerste and Savage
C. thompsoni Miller and Furnish
C. alcocki sp. nov.

On South Knife River the formation extends for 6 miles, from near locality 25294 to 25301 (Fig. 4). Contacts at both its eastern and western edges are not exposed. Member No. 1 is known only from a very small unfossiliferous sandstone outcrop about three-fourths of a mile above locality 25294. Member No. 2 is fossiliferous and has the same lithology as it has on Churchill River. Because most outcrops are low and at bends in the meandering South Knife its total thickness is unknown. The minimum thickness is 8 feet, and the maximum would probably be on the order of 20 feet. The following fossils are present:

Incertae sedis
Receptaculites sp.

Corals
Palaeophyllum stokesi (Milne-Edwards and Haime)
Grewingkia robusta (Whiteaves)
Saffordophyllum(?) portagechutense sp. nov.
Calapoecia arctica Troedsson(?)
Plasmopora lambei Schuchert
Catenipora robusta Sinclair and Bolton
C. aequabilis (Teichert)
C. agglomeratiformis (Whitfield)
Manipora amicarum Sinclair
M. feildeni (Etheridge)

Brachiopods
Diceromyonia sp.
Thaerodonta sp.

Gastropods
Trochonema coxi Wilson
Holopea gigantea sp. nov.
Hormotoma winnipegensis Whiteaves
Maclurites manitobensis (Whiteaves)
M. altus Wilson
Fusispira gigantea Wilson

Cephalopods
Lambeoceras landerense Foerste
L. baffinense Miller, Youngquist, and Collinson
Whiteavesites winnipegensis (Whiteaves)
Digenuoceras latum (Foerste)
Westonoceras nelsonense Foerste and Savage
Winnipegoceras laticurvatum (Whiteaves)
W. dowlingi Foerste
Cyrtogomphoceras turgidum Troedsson
C. rotundum Miller
C. foerstei Miller and Furnish
Charactoceras manitobense sp. nov.

On North Knife River the Portage Chute Formation is exposed for 1½ miles, about 30 miles from the mouth (Figs. 1, 4). It rests on steeply dipping peneplaned Precambrian argillites.

Along this river Member No. 1 is noticeably thicker than along other rivers, carries conglomerate beds, and is, in places, fossiliferous. It consists of about 12 feet of sandstone, calcareous sandstone, and minor amounts of conglomerate. Th member extends over all the outcrop area but is fossiliferous only in the west. Fossil described from this river by Miller and Youngquist (1947b) are probably from sand-

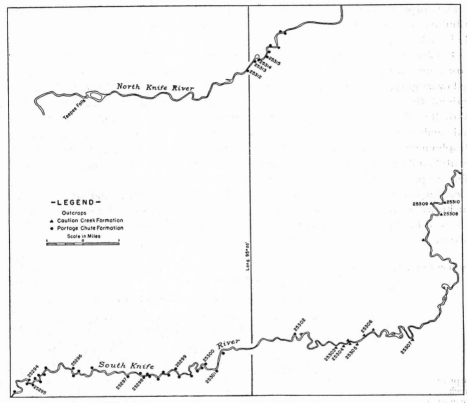

FIGURE 4. Map of North and South Knife rivers showing fossil localities and principal outcrop areas of Ordovician

stone outcrops at localities 25313 and 25314. The writer has identified the following:

Incertae sedis
  Receptaculites sp.

Corals
  Palaeophyllum halysitoides (Wilson)
  Grewingkia robusta (Whiteaves)
  Favistella alveolata (Goldfuss)
  Nyctopora(?) *foerstei* Bassler
  N. mackenziei sp. nov.
  Calapoecia arctica Troedsson(?)
  Plasmopora lambei Schuchert

Catenipora aequabilis (Teichert)
C. agglomeratiformis (Whitfield)

Brachiopod
  Diceromyonia sp.

Gastropods
  Trochonema coxi Wilson
  Maclurites manitobensis (Whiteaves)
  Fusispira gigantea Wilson
Cephalopods
  Kochoceras sp. I
  Lambeoceras kronlundi Miller and Youngquist

Member No. 2, which has the same lithology as on other rivers, occurs only at localities 25313 and 25314. Erosion has probably removed part of the unit, for the ly 6 feet. Fossils found are *Receptaculites* sp., *Grewingkia robusta*)iceromyonia sp.

SURPRISE CREEK FORMATION

e Creek Formation is named for its type section, a small steep-walled Churchill River (Pl. 1). Other good exposures of the formation are at Rapids and Hidden Creek.

rchill River the formation conformably overlies the Portage Chute and is ormably overlain by the Caution Creek Formation. It consists of light- sh-gray, micro- to cryptocrystalline, in many places cherty, dolomitic limestone ut the fragmental content that characterizes the Portage Chute Formation. h this change in lithology there is a profound change in fauna. The coralline d molluscan faunas of the Portage Chute are replaced by a predominantly trophomenid brachiopod fauna of the Surprise Creek. The disappearance of fragmental content suggests that the Surprise Creek was deposited in quieter, and possibly deeper waters than the Portage Chute.

At Surprise Creek the formation is divided into seven members and attains a gross thickness of 63.5 feet. These members can be recognized over the limited outcrop extent of the formation on Churchill River. In descending order, the succession is as follows:

			Feet
Caution Creek Formation			42.0
. . . . Paraconformity			
	Member		
	7	Limestone, dolomitic, buff, microcrystalline to fine-grained in massive buff weathering beds	4.5
	6	Limestone, dolomitic to dolomite, light yellowish gray, microcrystalline to fine-grained, in massive gray weathering beds	2.0
	5	Limestone, slightly dolomitic, light yellowish gray, cryptocrystalline, gray to dark gray weathering; and limestone, slightly dolomitic, microcrystalline. Alternating in regular beds 2 inches thick. Chert abundant in upper part	4.0
Surprise Creek Formation	4	Limestone, slightly dolomitic, light yellowish gray to buff, crypto- to microcrystalline, some organic debris, gray weathering, mottled with irregularly shaped rusty blotches in lower half; in upper half blotches are more regular in shape and lie parallel to bedding.	21.0
	3	Limestone, slightly dolomitic, light yellowish gray, microcrystalline, finely laminated, gray to brown weathering in regular beds 1–3 inches thick. Contains numerous lenses of chert	8.0
	2	Limestone, slightly dolomitic, light yellowish gray, microcrystalline, buff to gray weathering, breaking in irregular platy blocks, 1–2 inches thick. Contains a few lenticular lenses of chert in upper part	10.0
		Gap in exposures (covered interval)	2.0
	1	Limestone, slightly dolomitic, light yellowish gray, microcrystalline, fossiliferous, buff to gray weathering, breaking in irregular platy slabs 1–2 inches thick	12.0
. . . . Gradational contact			
Portage Chute Formation		Limestone, slightly dolomitic, light gray, microcrystalline, light gray to buff weathering with abundant organic detritus	8.0
. . . . Water level of Churchill River			

Member No. 1 is the only fossiliferous unit of the formation on Churchill River. Most fossils are molds of brachiopods and cannot be identified with certainty. The following fauna has been recognized:

Corals
  Lobocorallium goniophylloides (Teichert)
  Plasmopora lambei Schuchert

Brachiopods
  Rafinesquina lata Whiteaves
  R. lata Whiteaves var.
  R. pronis Roy
  Megamyonia raymondi (Bradley)(?)
  M. nitens (Billings)(?)

Thaerondonta sp.
Strophomena planocorrugata Twenhofel
S. hecuba Billings(?)
S. fluctuosa Billings(?)
S. spp. nov.
Rhynchotrema kananaskia Wilson(?)
Hypsiptycha janea (Billings)(?)

Gastropod
  Trochonema coxi Wilson

A prolonged search in other beds disclosed only one fossil: a *Beatricea nodulosa* Billings from Member No. 5.

Elsewhere the formation has been recognized only on Nelson River where it extends intermittently from locality 25259 to about 2 miles below locality 25264. The best exposures are at Lower Limestone Rapids.

Two lithologic divisions are recognized on Nelson River (Lower Member and Upper Member). Exact correlation with members at the type section is uncertain. The contact of the Lower Member with the underlying Portage Chute Formation is not exposed. Field relationships near the presumed contact suggest that the lower beds may grade laterally into the upper part of the Portage Chute Formation.

The Lower Member essentially embraces beds that Savage and Van Tuyl (1919) designated as "unit" 5 of the succession along Nelson River. (*See* Previous Work.) It is at least 20 feet thick and consists of light-gray-weathering, in some places cherty, light-yellowish-gray, microcrystalline, dolomitic limestone in irregular layers 1–2 inches thick. Fragmental material is present in the member but is less abundant than in the underlying Portage Chute Formation. The fauna is more varied than at the type section. The following fossils have been identified:

Corals
  Lobocorallium goniophylloides (Teichert)
  Nyctopora mackenziei sp. nov.
  Calapoecia anticostiensis Billings
  Plasmopora lambei Schuchert
  Catenipora robusta (Wilson)
  C. aequabilis (Teichert)

Brachiopods
  Rafinesquina lata Whiteaves
  Thaerodonta sp.
  Strophomena fluctuosa Billings(?)

S. sp., cf. *S. amoena* Wang
S. sp., cf. *S. concordensis* Foerste
Rhynchotrema kananaskia Wilson(?)

Gastropod
  Maclurites manitobensis (Whiteaves)

Cephalopods
  Narthecoceras crassisiphonatum (Whiteaves)
  Lambeoceras walkeri sp. nov.
  Whiteavesites procteri sp. nov.

The Upper Member occurs only in the vicinity of Lower Limestone Rapids and is made up of the beds Savage and Van Tuyl called "unit" 6 of the Nelson River succession. It is gradational into the underlying member and consists of at least 10 feet of conchoidally breaking, gray- to buff-weathering, light-yellowish-gray, microcrystalline, in places cryptocrystalline, dolomitic limestone. Organic detritus is rare or lacking. Lithologically it is similar to members No. 1 and 2 of the formation at the type section. The fauna is dominantly strophomenid and consists of the following brachiopods:

Rafinesquina lata Whiteaves
Megamyonia nitens (Billings)(?)
Thaerodonta spp.
Strophomena lenta Troedsson
Rhynchotrema kananaskia Wilson(?)

CHURCHILL RIVER GROUP

GENERAL STATEMENT

The Churchill River Group extends for about 30 miles on Churchill River, from near Hidden Creek down to Limestone Rapids. The total thickness is estimated at 180–200 feet.

The group occurs in two main areas along Churchill River, separated by a 4-mile gap in exposure between localities 25282 and 25283. The first area is in the stretch from Hidden Creek to locality 25282, and the second from 25283 to Red Head Rapids. The Caution Creek Formation and lower part of the Chasm Creek Formation are well exposed in the first area. Only upper beds of the Chasm Creek Formation are known in the second, and because they tend to occur as low scattered outcrops interpretation of thickness and succession is difficult.

The group is not complete on other rivers. Only the Caution Creek Formation is exposed on South Knife River, and only the Chasm Creek on the Nelson.

CAUTION CREEK FORMATION

The Caution Creek Formation has its type section at Caution Creek, a small tributary of the Churchill. Excellent exposures also occur at Hidden Creek, Surprise Creek, Chasm Creek, and locality 25282 (Pl. 1; Pl. 2, fig. 2).

On Churchill River the formation consists of 42 feet of dolomitic limestone and is divided into three conformable members designated, in ascending order, as Members No. 1, 2, and 3.

Member No. 1 is 18 feet thick and consists mostly of gray- to yellowish-gray-weathering, light-yellowish-gray, cryptocrystalline, slightly dolomitic limestone, weathering in irregular, rather rubbly beds about 1 inch thick. Shelly detritus is plentiful in the limestone. The contact with the underlying Surprise Creek Formation appears paraconformable.

Member No. 1 is the most fossiliferous unit in the Hudson Bay Ordovician succession and has a varied fauna, largely of corals, brachiopods, gastropods, and cephalopods. The following have been identified:

Corals
  Palaeophyllum raduguini n. nov.
  Lobocorallium trilobatum var. *major* nov.
  Deiracorallium manitobense sp. nov.
  Bighornia patella (Wilson)
  Lyopora manitobensis sp. nov.
  Calapoecia anticostiensis Billings
  C. canadensis var. *ungava* Cox
  Protrochiscolithus kiaeri Troedsson
  Palaeofavosites capax (Billings)

Favosites wilsonae sp. nov.
Catenipora rubra Sinclair and Bolton
C. robusta (Wilson)
C. foerstei sp. nov.
Manipora amicarum Sinclair

Brachiopods
  Plaesiomys occidentalis (Okulitch)
  Megamyonia raymondi (Bradley)
  M. nitens (Billings)

FIGURE 1. Churchill River, view upstream. Bad Cache Rapids in foreground. Portage Chute Formation exposed along river bank to left; rubbly outcrops of overlying Surprise Creek Formation in upper left foreground.

FIGURE 2. Chasm Creek, small tributary of Churchill River, showing contact between recessive Caution Creek Formation and overlying massive Chasm Creek Formation. Pronounced bedding plane just above man's head marks contact between Members No. 2 and 3 of Caution Creek Formation.

CHURCHILL RIVER AREA, MANITOBA, CANADA

FIGURE 1. Nelson River, view downstream from above Upper Limestone Rapids.
Ice and snow-covered banks are typical of river during June.

FIGURE 2. South Knife River, view upstream from fossil locality 25305
showing low rubbly outcrops of Caution Creek Formation.

NELSON AND SOUTH KNIFE RIVERS, MANITOBA, CANADA

M. ceres (Billings)
Strophomena planocorrugata Twenhofel
S. fluctuosa Billings
Lepidocyclus perlamellosus (Whitfield)
L. capax (Conrad)
Hypsiptycha anticostiensis (Billings)
Zygospira resupinata Wang

Gastropods
  Trochonema coxi Wilson
  Liospira parva Wilson

Cephalopods
  Cyclendoceras belli sp. nov.
  Lambeoceras nudum Troedsson
  Ephippiorthoceras dowlingi Foerste and Savage
  Probillingsites harkeri sp. nov.
  Billingsites borealis (Parks)
  B. keatingi sp. nov.
  B. canadensis (Billings)(?)
  Digenuoceras mclearni sp. nov.
  Winnipegoceras(?) *contractum* (Foerste and Savage)
  Charactoceras laddi Foerste
  C. warrenae sp. nov.

Member No. 2 is also 18 feet thick. The rock is gray- to brown-weathering, light-yellowish-gray, crypto- to microcrystalline, slightly dolomitic limestone and occurs in rather smooth layers about 1–2 inches thick. Organic detritus is relatively rare. Strophomenids constitute the bulk of the fauna. Fossils identified are as follows:

Plaesiomys occidentalis (Okulitch)
Megamyonia nitens (Billings)
M. ceres (Billings)
Strophomena planocorrugata Twenhofel
S. fluctuosa Billings
S. elongata James(?)
S. sp. nov.
Lepidocyclus perlamellosus (Whitfield)
L. gigas Wang(?)
Zygospira resupinata Wang

Member No. 3 consists of 6 feet of gray earthy-weathering, light-yellowish-gray, microcrystalline, almost cryptocrystalline, slightly dolomitic limestone, weathering in rather nodular beds 1–2 inches thick (Pl. 2, fig. 2). The fauna is more varied than that of the underlying member and consists of:

Corals
  Lobocorallium trilobatum var. *major* nov.
  Bighornia patella (Wilson)
  Palaeofavosites alveolaris (Lonsdale)(?)
  Favosites wilsonae sp. nov.

Brachiopods
  Plaesiomys occidentalis (Okulitch)
  Megamyonia nitens (Billings)
  M. ceres (Billings)
  Lepidocyclus perlamellosus (Whitfield)
  Hypsiptycha anticostiensis (Billings)

Cephalopods
  Charactocerina goodwini sp. nov.

Elsewhere in the northern Lowland the Caution Creek Formation has been recognized only on South Knife River where it crops out intermittently over a distance of 9 miles from locality 25302 to 25310. The formation is best exposed in the interval from locality 25303 to 25307 (Pl. 3, fig. 2). Contact relationships with underlying formations are unknown because of a 2-mile gap in exposures to the west. The Surprise Creek Formation may underlie this gap.

Two lithologic divisions are recognized within the formation on the South Knife and are designated as the Lower and Upper members. These members have not been correlated with those of the type section.

The Lower Member has a minimum thickness of 6 feet and consists of conchoidally weathering, light-gray, cryptocrystalline limestone. Its meager fauna, which is not diagnostic in correlation, consists of *Strophomena planocorrugata* Twenhofel, *Lepido-*

cyclus capax (Conrad), and *Desmograptus canadensis* (Whiteaves). The last species is elsewhere known only from the Cat Head Member of the Red River and suggests that the member may belong in the Surprise Creek Formation. Dendroid graptolites are typically long ranging, however, so that more stress is given *L. capax*, and the Lower Member is questionably placed in the Caution Creek Formation.

The more widespread Upper Member is lithologically similar to Member No. 1 of the formation on Churchill River. It has a minimum thickness of 16 feet. The maximum may be 20–30 feet. It consists of gray- and orange-weathering, light-yellowish-gray, crypto- to microcrystalline, slightly dolomitic limestone, in rubbly weathering beds 1–3 inches thick. Fragmental organic material is common, particularly in lower beds, and forms a fair proportion of the rock. Fossils identified from the Upper Member are as follows:

Stromatoporoid
  Aulacera undulata (Billings)

Corals
  Lobocorallium trilobatum var. *major* nov.
  Deiracorallium manitobense sp. nov.
  Bighornia patella (Wilson)
  Lyopora manitobensis sp. nov.
  Calapoecia anticostiensis Billings
  C. canadensis var. *ungava* Cox
  Protrochiscolithus kiaeri Troedsson
  Palaeofavosites alveolaris (Lonsdale)(?)
  P. capax (Billings)
  Favosites wilsonae sp. nov.
  Catenipora robusta (Wilson)
  C. foerstei sp. nov.
  Manipora amicarum Sinclair

Brachiopods
  Plaesiomys occidentalis (Okulitch)
  Megamyonia unicostata (Meek and Worthen)

M. nitens (Billings)
M. ceres (Billings)
Strophomena planocorrugata Twenhofel
S. hecuba Billings
S. fluctuosa Billings
Lepidocyclus perlamellosus (Whitfield)
Hypsiptycha anticostiensis (Billings)

Gastropods
  Trochonema coxi Wilson
  Liospira parva Wilson

Cephalopods
  Cyclendoceras belli sp. nov.
  Narthecoceras crassisiphonatum (Whiteaves)
  Parksoceras lepidodendroides (Parks)
  Lambeoceras nudum Troedsson
  Billingsites borealis (Parks)

Aulacera undulata (Billings) and *Narthecoceras crassisiphonatum* (Whiteaves) were collected from a small and isolated, sparsely fossiliferous outcrop area between localities 25308 and 25310. This fauna is anomalous in that the stromatoporoid is usually characteristic of the Chasm Creek Formation, whereas the cephalopod is more diagnostic of the Bad Cache Rapid Group. The beds from which they were collected, however, are thought to belong in the Caution Creek because they are lithologically similar to, and on strike with, the Upper Member cropping out up-river.

CHASM CREEK FORMATION

A complete section for the Chasm Creek Formation is not available at any one locality along the Churchill. The western outcrop area has the best exposures, but only of the lower part of the formation. In the eastern outcrop area, from locality 25283 to Red Head Rapids, higher beds are present but not well exposed. These beds are separated by the 4-mile gap in exposures from those in the western area. (*See* Churchill River Group.)

The formation is best exposed at Chasm Creek, a small gorge entering Churchill

River (Pl. 2, fig. 2). Here only 44 feet of beds is present. Down-river, in the eastern outcrop area, are higher beds with an estimated thickness of about 140 feet. Therefore the formation is probably about 180 feet thick.

The formation is divided into four apparently conformable members designated in ascending order as Members Nos. 1, 2, 3, 4.

Member No. 1 is at least 55 feet thick. The lower 44 feet of the unit is well exposed at Chasm Creek and locality 25282 where it consists of very resistant, light-yellowish-gray to buff, microcrystalline, iron-rich, in many places fucoidal, dolomitic to slightly dolomitic limestone, in massive beds weathering yellow and orange. Organic detritus is rather sparse and finely fragmented. The contact with the underlying Caution Creek Formation is conformable, but the faunal aspect of the Chasm Creek is different as corals are the most abundant fossils. The following fauna has been identified:

Corals
Lobocorallium trilobatum var. *major* nov.
Deiracorallium manitobense sp. nov.
D. manitobense var. *churchillense* nov.
Bighornia patella (Wilson)
B. solearis (Ladd)
B. bottei sp. nov.
Lyopora manitobensis sp. nov.
L. churchillensis sp. nov.
Calapoecia anticostiensis Billings
C. canadensis var. *ungava* Cox
Palaeofavosites alveolaris (Lonsdale)(?)
P. prolificus (Billings)
P. capax (Billings)
Catenipora robusta (Wilson)
Manipora amicarum Sinclair

Brachiopods
Diceromyonia storeya (Okulitch)
Megamyonia nitens (Billings)
M. breviuscula (Foerte)
Thaerodonta sp.
Lepidocyclus perlamellosus (Whitfield)
Hypsiptycha anticostiensis (Billings)

Gastropod
Trochonema coxi Wilson

Cephalopod
Kochoceras bailliei sp. nov.

At localities 25283 and 25284, 11 feet of massive beds, lithologically and faunally similar to Member No. 1, is considered the uppermost beds of the member and stratigraphically higher than those at Chasm Creek. *Palaeofavosites okulitchi* Stearn appears for the first time. This species is considered diagnostic for the upper Stony Mountain Formation (Gunton Member) of southern Manitoba and suggests that these upper beds of Member No. 1 and the higher strata of the formation may correlate with the Gunton. Fossils identified are as follows:

Corals
Palaeophyllum stokesi (Milne-Edwards and Haime)
P. raduguini n. nov.
Lobocorallium trilobatum var. *major* nov.
Bighornia patella (Wilson)
B. bottei sp. nov.
Favistella alveolata (Goldfuss)
Lyopora manitobensis sp. nov.
L. churchillensis sp. nov.
Calapoecia anticostiensis Billings
Palaeofavosites capax (Billings)
P. okulitchi Stearn

Manipora amicarum Sinclair
M. irregularis (Teichert)

Brachiopods
Plaesiomys occidentalis (Okulitch)
Megamyonia nitens (Billings)
Lepidocyclus perlamellosus (Whitfield)

Gastropod
Trochonema coxi Wilson

Cephalopods
Fremontoceras sp., cf. *F. loperi* Foerste
Apsidoceras milleri sp. nov.

Member No. 2 is poorly exposed and occurs intermittently along the river bank as low rubbly outcrops. Lithologically it is similar to Member No. 1 but is less resistant and tends to be lighter-colored both on weathered and fresh surfaces. Typically it is a light-gray-weathering, light-gray, crypto- to microcrystalline, dolomitic to slightly dolomitic limestone containing a fair amount of finely fragmented organic detritus, and estimated to be about 100 feet thick. The fauna consists for the most part of corals. Cephalopods are locally abundant and show strong Red River affinities. The following species have been identified:

Stromatoporoid
  Beatricea nodulosa Billings

Corals
  Palaeophyllum raduguini n. nov.
  Lobocorallium trilobatum var. *major* nov.
  Deiracorallium giganteum sp. nov.
  Bighornia bottei sp. nov.
  Lyopora churchillensis sp. nov.
  Calapoecia anticostiensis Billings
  Protrochiscolithus kiaeri Troedsson
  Palaeofavosites alveolaris (Lonsdale)(?)
  P. prolificus (Billings)
  P. okulitchi Stearn
  Catenipora sp.
  Manipora amicarum Sinclair

Brachiopods
  Megamyonia nitens (Billings)
  Lepidocyclus perlamellosus (Whitfield)

Gastropod
  Trochonema coxi Wilson

Cephalopods
  Kochoceras bailliei sp. nov.
  Paractinoceras(?) *churchillense* sp. nov.
  Gorbyoceras giganteum sp. nov.
  Digenuoceras okulitchi sp. nov.
  Winnipegoceras callahani sp. nov.

Member No. 3 is 15 feet thick and is exposed only at locality 25290. Except for the addition of several rather massive, light-gray, cryptocrystalline, organic-free dolomitic limestone interbeds, it is lithologically similar to Member No. 2. Most of the fauna consists of corals and cephalopods. The following species have been identified:

Stromatoporoids
  Beatricea clarki sp. nov.
  Aulacera undulata (Billings)

Corals
  Lobocorallium trilobatum var. *major* nov.
  Bighornia bottei sp. nov.
  Phaulactis stummi sp. nov.
  Lyopora manitobensis sp. nov.
  Calapoecia canadensis var. *ungava* Cox
  Palaeofavosites okulitchi Stearn
  Manipora amicarum Sinclair

Gastropod
  Trochonema coxi Wilson

Cephalopods
  Kochoceras bailliei sp. nov.
  K. giganteum sp. nov.
  Huronia septata Parks
  Digenuoceras okulitchi sp. nov.
  Antiplectoceras shamattawaense (Parks)
  Charactocerina leithi sp. nov.

Member No. 4 is exposed mainly around Red Head Rapids, although a small section crops out at Limestone Rapids. The member is distinct from underlying units of the formation in that it is strongly dolomitic. It consists of well-bedded, light-gray-weathering, microcrystalline, highly fucoidal light-gray dolomite in layers 1–2 inches thick. It is thought to be related to the Chasm Creek Formation, because the rather obscure contact relationships suggest that it is probably conformable with Member No. 3. The known measured thickness is 11 feet; the estimated maximum is 20 feet. The member is practically unfossiliferous. The only species identified are *Strophomena arcuata* Shaler(?) and *Kinaschukoceras churchillense* gen. et sp. nov. The latter is characteristic of the unit.

Other outcrops definitely referable to the Chasm Creek Formation have been found only on Nelson River. The formation here extends intermittently for about 6 miles from locality 25267 to the mouth of Angling River. The beds correspond generally to Savage and Van Tuyls' (1919) "unit" 7 (Shamattawa Formation) of the Nelson River succession. (*See* Previous Work.) The main outcrops occur at localities 25267 and 25268 and at the mouth of Angling River. The formation has a minimum thickness of 15 feet and consists mainly of gray-weathering, light-brownish-gray, cryptocrystalline to fine-grained, dolomitic to slightly dolomitic limestone. Organic detritus is plentiful. The fauna does not allow exact correlation with the Chasm Creek Formation on Churchill River. Intermingling of species, some of which are found in Member No. 2 and others in Member No. 3 on Churchill River, suggests that the beds may correlate with parts of one or both of these members. Species identified are as follows:

Stromatoporoids
  Beatricea nodulosa Billings
  B. clarki sp. nov.
  Aulacera undulata (Billings)

Corals
  Lobocorallium trilobatum var. *major* nov.
  Bighornia bottei sp. nov.
  Favistella alveolata var. *stellaris* (Wilson)
  Lyopora manitobensis sp. nov.
  L. churchillensis sp. nov.
  Protrochiscolithus kiaeri Troedsson
  Palaeofavosites capax (Billings)
  P. alveolaris (Lonsdale) (?)

Catenipora rubra Sinclair and Bolton
  C. robusta (Wilson)

Brachiopod
  Megamyonia nitens (Billings)

Gastropod
  Trochonema coxi Wilson

Cephalopods
  Huronia septata Parks
  Digenuoceras okulitchi sp. nov.
  Apsidoceras boreale Foerste and Savage

RED HEAD RAPIDS FORMATION

The Red Head Rapids Formation has been recognized only along Churchill River where it crops out intermittently for 12 miles from Red Head Rapids to locality 25293. Below the last locality the river is devoid of exposures for about 40 miles as far as Port Churchill where Silurian and some questionable Ordovician lie on Precambrian.

Two members are recognized. The lower, Member No. 1, is best exposed around Red Head Rapids. It is easily recognizable and consists of orange-weathering, light-yellow, microcrystalline dolomite typically in very tabular beds 1–2 inches thick. The estimated thickness is 25 feet. It overlies the Chasm Creek Formation with an abrupt change in lithology, suggestive of a paraconformity. No fossils have been found in the member.

Member No. 2 is known only from locality 25293, where it has a minimum thickness of 17 feet. The unit consists of gray-weathering, gray to yellowish-gray, microcrystalline dolomite in beds 2 inches–1½ feet thick. Drift obscures the contact with Member No. 1. Lithologically both members are similar to Silurian near Port Churchill, but two poorly preserved fossils in Member No. 2, identified as *Calapoecia* sp. and *Kochoceras* sp. II, suggest that the formation may be Ordovician. On the basis of its stratigraphic position and these fossils the formation is questionably correlated with the Stonewall Formation of southern Manitoba.

CORRELATION

The Ordovician strata of the northern Hudson Bay Lowland, particularly those on Churchill River, contain one of the most complete successions found in the Arctic Ordovician faunal province. Two divisions are present. The lower, represented by the Bad Cache Rapids Group of Middle or Late Ordovician age, has been recognized over wide areas of northern and western North America (Nelson, 1959a; 1959b). It is present as the Red River Formation in southern Manitoba, the Whitewood of South Dakota, the Lower and Middle members of the Bighorn of Wyoming, the Lower and Middle members of the Fremont of Colorado, and the Frobisher Bay outlier of Baffin Island. These strata have received a great deal of attention because of their puzzling fauna with both Middle and Late Ordovician affinities. The fauna, often termed "Arctic" or "Boreal", is easily recognizable by its content of *Receptaculites* and *Catenipora* associated with large gastropods and cephalopods belonging to such genera as *Maclurites*, *Hormotoma*, *Cyrtogomphoceras*, *Whiteavesites*, *Winnipegoceras*, *Digenuoceras*, and *Kochoceras*.

The upper division, represented by the Churchill River Group has also been recognized over extensive areas of North America but has received relatively little attention. It is known as the Stony Mountain Formation in southern Manitoba, the Beaverfoot of British Columbia, and the Upper Member of both the Bighorn and Fremont formations of Wyoming and Colorado, respectively. The fauna is easily recognizable and is considered of Richmondian age. Typically it consists of *Catenipora* and radially asymmetrical cup corals of the genera *Lobocorallium*, *Deiracorallium*, and *Bighornia* associated with Anticosti Island species of *Palaeofavosites* and brachiopods. Cephalopods, except locally, are rather rare and related to those of the underlying Red River equivalents.

Miller, Youngquist, and Collinson (1954) have reviewed and correlated the Arctic Ordovician, particularly that of the Red River Formation and coeval strata. The present report deals with correlation only to southern Manitoba and the Gods River area of the Lowland.

ORDOVICIAN OF SOUTHERN MANITOBA

GENERAL STATEMENT

Four Ordovician formations are recognized in the Lake Winnipeg area of southern Manitoba (in ascending order): the Winnipeg, Red River, Stony Mountain, and Stonewall formations. Most data on lithology, thickness, and subdivisions of these formations (Fig. 2) have been compiled from reports of Dowling (1900), Foerste (1928; 1929), Okulitch (1943), Baillie (1951; 1952), Stearn (1956), Sinclair and Leith (1958), Sinclair (1959), and Porter and Fuller (1959). Until recently three members constituted the Red River Formation (in ascending order): Dog Head, Cat Head, and Selkirk. Sinclair (1959) has shown that the Selkirk is part of the Dog Head and accordingly recommended suppression of the name. His interpretation is followed in Figure 2.

The age of the conformable Winnipeg and Red River formations has been the subject of considerable controversy. Excellent summaries of the problem and history of dating are given by Roy (1941), Miller, Youngquist, and Collinson (1954), Flower (1957), and Flower and Teichert (1957). Some workers, notably Kay (1935; *in* Twenhofel, 1954), Flower (1952), and Sinclair (1956a), consider the two formations Middle Ordovician, whereas others, particularly Foerste (1928; 1929; 1935), Miller (1930; 1932), Miller, Youngquist, and Collinson (1954), and Sweet and Miller (1957) consider them Upper Ordovician. The Winnipeg Formation is relatively barren, and thus most discussions about age have revolved about the fossiliferous Red River Formation.

The Red River fauna is anomalous in that it contains a large proportion of species, notably brachiopods, gastropods, and trilobites, which are either Middle Ordovician or have Middle Ordovician affinities, whereas the generic affinities of many of the associated corals and cephalopods are generally considered to be with the Richmondian.

Early workers such as Whiteaves (1897) and Dowling (1900) stressed the Middle Ordovician species, and the Red River and Winnipeg were placed in the Middle Ordovician. This dating was generally accepted for nearly 30 years. Foerste (1928; 1929; Foerste and Savage, 1927) suggested that the Red River corals and particularly the cephalopods have strong Richmondian affinities and regarded the Middle Ordovician species as recurrent. The two formations were accordingly placed in the Richmondian stage. At present there is a tendency to regard the Red River as either low in the Upper Ordovician (Miller, Youngquist, and Collinson, 1954; Sweet, 1954; 1955; Duncan, 1957) or Middle Ordovician (Kay, 1935 *in* Twenhofel, 1954; Flower, 1952; Sinclair, 1956a). Most of this dating has been done by reference to sections outside Manitoba considered correlative with the Red River.

Workers who favor the lower Upper Ordovician position (Eden and/or Maysville) for the Red River do so because it seems the best compromise to explain the association of Middle Ordovician species with Richmondian-like genera of corals and cephalopods. Those who support a Middle Ordovician age claim that the Richmondian affinities of the corals and cephalopods are open to question and that they actually have Middle Ordovician affinities.

The Stony Mountain and Stonewall formations have not been the subject of extended discussion. The Stony Mountain is generally considered Richmondian, but Okulitch (1943, p. 68) suggested that the upper part [Gunton and Birse members = Gunton of Baillie (1952)] may be Gamachian. Until recently the Stonewall had been placed in the Silurian, but fossils indicate a Late Ordovician age (Stearn, 1953; 1956).

The Bad Cache Rapids and Churchill River groups of the Hudson Bay Lowland are correlated with various members of the Red River and Stony Mountain formations. Faunal evidence indicates that the Bad Cache Rapids correlates with the Red River, and the Churchill River Group with the Stony Mountain, and that the Bad Cache Rapids–Red River strata may be closely related in time to the overlying

Churchill River–Stony Mountain strata. Because the latter units are considered high Richmondian, a Late Ordovician age is suggested for the Bad Cache Rapids and Red River strata. The "Edenian and Maysvillian" stages may represent a much shorter interval of time than formerly considered, because Flower (1956; 1957) has suggested that "Eden" is but a facies of the Trenton. Thus, although the Bad Cache Rapids–Red River may be related in time to the overlying Churchill River–Stony Mountain strata, the former could be Middle Ordovician if these two stages have little time value. Until Flower's suggestion is verified it will be here assumed that the type Eden and Maysville have significant time value.

BAD CACHE RAPIDS GROUP

The Portage Chute Formation is correlated with the Dog Head Member of the Red River Formation (Fig. 2) because of eight species restricted to both. These are *Hormotoma winnipegensis*, *Maclurites ungava*, *Paractinoceras canadense*, *Whiteavesites winnipegensis*, *Billingsites costulatus*, *Digenuoceras latum*, *Winnipegoceras laticurvatum*, and *W. dowlingi*. The lithology and faunal associates of these two units are also similar.

The Surprise Creek Formation cannot be accurately correlated with members of the Red River Formation because of lack of diagnostic species. On the basis of its stratigraphic position and lithology, however, it is considered to correlate questionably with the Cat Head Member of southern Manitoba. The evolution of the genus *Lobocorallium* (*see* Systematic Paleontology) suggests that the time interval represented by the paraconformity between the Surprise Creek and basal beds of the Churchill River Group may be short.

CHURCHILL RIVER GROUP

The Churchill River Group is considered equivalent to nearly the whole of the Stony Mountain Formation of southern Manitoba. Detailed correlation is difficult, however, because many long-ranging species in the Churchill River Group have restricted ranges in the Stony Mountain, and vice versa. The combined fauna of the Caution Creek and the lower 44 feet of Member No. 1 of the Chasm Creek Formation, however, are very similar to that of the combined Stony Mountain Shale (= Gunn) and Penitentiary members of southern Manitoba which have nine species common to both. These are *Deiracorallium manitobense*, *Bighornia patella*, *Diceromyonia storeya*, *Plaesiomys occidentalis*, *Hypsiptycha anticostiensis*, *Lepidocyclus capax*, *Megamyonia nitens*, *Strophomena planocorrugata*, and *Liospira parva*.

The fauna of the upper 11 feet of Member No. 1 of the Chasm Creek and higher members of this formation is generally different from that of the Gunton Member of the Stony Mountain Formation. *Palaeofavosites okulitchi*, however, first appears in the upper 11 feet of Member No. 1, and also in the basal beds of the Gunton of southern Manitoba. In southern Manitoba *Antiplectoceras shamattawaense* first appears in the upper part of the Gunton Member (Birse Member of Okulitch, 1943) and in northern Manitoba within the upper part (Member No. 3) of the Chasm Creek Formation.

RED HEAD RAPIDS FORMATION

Correlation of the Red Head Rapids Formation is uncertain. A Silurian age is suggested by the abrupt, paraconformable-appearing contact with the underlying Chasm Creek Formation and by the lithology. The lithology of the Red Head Rapids is very similar to Silurian near Port Churchill, about 40 miles distant. The two poorly preserved fossils from the formation, however, identified as *Calapoecia* sp. and *Kochoceras* sp. II are generally considered Ordovician. The Red Head Rapids is thus questionably considered Ordovician and may correlate, on the basis of its stratigraphic position, with the Stonewall Formation of southern Manitoba.

AGE OF BAD CACHE RAPIDS GROUP

The fauna of the Bad Cache Rapids Group is generally distinct from that of the overlying Churchill River Group. Certain genera and species, however, occur in both and suggest that the two groups may be closely related in time. Species in common are *Palaeophyllum stokesi, Calapoecia anticostiensis, Catenipora rubra, C. robusta,* and *Manipora amicarum.* The genera are *Palaeophyllum, Catenipora, Manipora, Kochoceras, Lambeoceras, Narthecoceras, Billingsites, Digenuoceras, Winnipegoceras, Charactoceras, Charactocerina,* and (?)*Paractinoceras.* Close temporal relationship between the two groups is also suggested by the evolutionary lineage of *Lobocorallium.* (*See* Systematic Paleontology.) The time necessary for the weakly trilobate *L. goniophylloides* of the Surprise Creek Formation to give rise to the more strongly trilobate *L. trilobatum* var. *major* of the overlying Churchill River Group is probably relatively short, judging by the rate of evolution from *Grewingkia robusta* of the Portage Chute Formation into *L. goniophylloides.* (*See* Systematic Paleontology.)

Since the Churchill River Group is considered high Richmondian and possibly part Gamachian, a low Richmondian and/or Maysvillian age would be appropriate for the Bad Cache Rapids Group. If the former group is actually low Richmondian, then the latter is probably restricted to part of the Maysvillian, Edenian, or Trentonian. The Late Ordovician age assignment for the Bad Cache Rapids would seem most reasonable because of the occurrence of *Beatricea nodulosa* (a Richmondian species) in the Surprise Creek Formation. The brachiopod species of the Surprise Creek Formation also suggest a Late Ordovician age for the group, but in the writer's opinion little stress should be placed upon them because of their poor preservation.

Comparison of the Bad Cache Rapids and coeval Red River coral and cephalopod fauna with those occurring in undisputed Middle and Upper Ordovician rocks leads to some interesting speculations. For many years the Richmondian age of the Red River Formation was based partly on the abundance of *Catenipora.* Sinclair and Bolton (1956), however, have indicated that, although rare, the genus is relatively more characteristic of Middle Ordovician rocks in Eastern North America. *Catenipora,* however, is very abundant in Richmondian strata of Stony Mountain age in northern and western North America, although absent from type Stony Mountain (a facies phenomenon?).

The cephalopod genera of the Red River were formerly considered to have Richmondian affinities. Sinclair (1956a), however, stated that the Red River was probably Middle Ordovician, as Flower (1952) had noted that certain cephalopods (*Lambeoceras, Diestoceras, Winnipegoceras, Fremontoceras*) of the Middle Ordovician Terrebonne and related horizons are characteristic Red River genera. The first two occur in both undisputed Middle and Upper Ordovician rocks so that they have little bearing on the problem of dating the Red River. As Flower indicated, the Terrebonne *Winnipegoceras* is probably primitive in comparison with Red River forms. His "*Fremontoceras*" does not fit Foerste's (1935) generic description (*see* Systematic Paleontology) but might be considered a primitive representative of the genus.

Flower noted that only *Huronia* and *Billingsites* of the Red River cephalopod genera had Richmondian affinities. The Richmondian Churchill River Group of the Lowland, however, contains a considerable assemblage of Red River genera so far not found in Middle Ordovician rocks. Besides *Huronia* and *Billingsites* the following occur: *Kochoceras, Digenuoceras, Ephippiorthoceras, Characterocerina, Fremontoceras, Paractinoceras,* and *Narthecoceras.* [The last two should be regarded with caution (*see* Systematic Paleontology) for the generic designation of *Paractinoceras* is in doubt, and the value of *Narthecoceras* as a true genus is doubtful.] In contrast, there are no genera (with the doubtful exceptions of *Allumettoceras* and *Lavaloceras*) common to only Red River and undoubted Middle Ordovician strata.

AGE OF CHURCHILL RIVER GROUP

Correlation of the Churchill River Group with the standard Richmond section of eastern Northern America is difficult because few species are common to both. Such species as *Beatricea nodulosa, Aulacera undulata, Lepidocyclus capax,* and *L. perlamellosus* suggest that the group is Richmondian. Most of the fauna, however, is either indigenous to the Stony Mountain Arctic faunal province (*see* Nelson, 1959a; 1959b) or are Anticosti Island species. Correlation with the Anticosti Island Upper Ordovician is unsatisfactory because most of the species that are short ranging in the Lowland are long ranging through the English Head, Vaureal, and Ellis Bay formations of Anticosti Island.

The Churchill River Group is considered high Richmondian and possibly in part Gamachian on the basis of *Favosites wilsonae* sp. nov. from the Caution Creek and *Phaulactis stummi* sp. nov. from the Chasm Creek Formation. Both *Favosites* and *Phaulactis* are typically Silurian genera, and their presence in the Churchill River Group suggests it is very high in the Ordovician. The only definitely recorded Ordovician *Favosites* (*F. forbesi*) in North America is from the Gamachian Ellis Bay Formation of Anticosti Island. This is also the only Ordovician formation that contains corals (*Cyathophyllum ellisense*) with peripheral structures similar to *Phaulactis.*

The writer believes the dating of the Anticosti Island succession will directly affect age interpretations for the Bad Cache Rapids and Churchill River groups and the respectively coeval Red River and Stony Mountain formations. It is here assumed, following the conclusions of Twenhofel (1928) and others that the English Head and Vaureal formations are Richmondian, and that the Ellis Bay Formation is Gamachian in age. The fauna of these formations is rather similar to that of the

Churchill River Group, and this suggests a Late Ordovician age for the Churchill River. If, however, the Anticosti Island formations are earlier Late Ordovician then the Churchill River Group would probably be older, and accordingly a Middle Ordovician age would be indicated for the Bad Cache Rapids Group. Sinclair (1956b) has interpreted the English Head Formation as low in the Upper Ordovician. No supporting data for his conclusion, however, have been published.

SHAMATTAWA FORMATION, GODS RIVER, NORTHERN MANITOBA

The type section of the Shamattawa Formation is along Gods River below the trading post of Shamattawa, 60 miles southeast of Nelson River. The formation was named and described by Savage and Van Tuyl (1919), although general discussions of stratigraphy and paleontology were earlier given by Tyrrell (1913) and Parks (1915; *in* Tyrrell, 1913).

As described by Savage and Van Tuyl the formation contains at least 40 feet of limestone divisible into two members. A long list of genera and species, many tentatively identified, was given by these authors. The cephalopod fauna was later fully described by Foerste and Savage (1927).

Savage and Van Tuyl correlated the Shamattawa with the Stony Mountain Formation of southern Manitoba. The fauna also indicates correlation with the Churchill River Group of the northern Lowland. Much of the fauna suggests correlation with the Caution Creek Formation, but two associated species (*Huronia septata* and *Antiplectoceras shamattawaense*) are considered diagnostic of the upper Chasm Creek Formation of the northern Lowland.

SYSTEMATIC PALEONTOLOGY

INTRODUCTORY REMARKS

The Ordovician fauna from the northern part of Hudson Bay Lowland is rich and varied and composed of chiefly *Receptaculites*, solitary and colonial corals, brachiopods, gastropods, and cephalopods. *Receptaculites* and brachiopods have been identified for purposes of correlation (*see* Stratigraphy and Correlation) but are not described here as the writer feels that their abundance and variability indicate a more detailed treatment than can be undertaken at present. The very abundant representatives of the cephalopod genus *Diestoceras* have also been reserved for later study.

Synoptic distribution of the species described from the Lowland is shown on Table 1.

Phylum COELENTERATA Frey and Leuckart
Class HYDROZOA Owen
Order STROMATOPOROIDEA Nicholson and Murie
Family AULACERIDAE Kühn
Genus *Beatricea* Billings, 1857
Type Species: *Beatricea nodulosa* Billings, 1857
Beatricea nodulosa Billings
(Pl. 4, fig. 3)

1857 *Beatricea nodulosa* BILLINGS, Geol. Surv. Canada Rept. Prog. 1853–1856, p. 344
1895 *Beatricea nodulosa* Billings. WHITEAVES, Geol. Surv. Canada Pal. Foss., v. 3, pt. 3, p. 114
1909 *Beatricea nodulosa* Billings. FOERSTE, Denison Univ. Bull., Jour. Sci. Lab., v. 14, p. 300
1910 *Beatricea nodulosa* Billings. PARKS, Univ. Toronto Studies, Geol. Ser., no. 7, p. 45, Pl. 25, figs. 2–5, 7, 8
1915 *Beatricea nodulosa* Billings. BASSLER, United States Nat. Mus. Bull. 92, v. 1, p. 113
1928 *Beatricea (Aulacera) nodulosa* Billings. TWENHOFEL, Geol. Surv. Canada Mem. 154, p. 106
1943 *Beatricea nodulosa* Billings. OKULITCH, Trans. Roy. Soc. Canada, v. 37, sec. 4, Pl. 2, fig. 2
1956 *Beatricea nodulosa* Billings. LECOMPTE, Treat. Invert. Pal., p. F, pt. 142, fig. 113: 1a, b

OCCURRENCE: One specimen (hypotype, G.S.C. No. 10557) from Member No. 5 of Surprise Creek Formation: locality 25278; and one from Member No. 2 of Chasm Creek Formation, Churchill River: locality 25285. One specimen from Chasm Creek Formation, Nelson River: locality 25267

DISCUSSION: *Beatricea nodulosa* was originally described from the Upper Ordovician of Anticosti Island. In southern Manitoba it occurs in the Birse interval of the Gunton Member, Stony Mountain Formation (Okulitch, 1943), and in the overlying Stonewall Formation (Baillie, 1951).

Beatricea clarki sp. nov.
(Pl. 4, figs. 1a–c, 2)

OCCURRENCE: Chasm Creek Formation: holotype (G.S.C. No. 10555) is from Member No. 3, Churchill River: locality 25290; paratype (G.S.C. No. 10556) from Nelson River: locality 25267

DESCRIPTION: Species includes Beatriceas subtriangular rather than circular in section. The three concave sides have nodes like those of *B. nodulosa*.

Interior divided into 3 zones. Central zone camerated axial tube approximately 5 mm wide. Surrounding this are concentric layers of cystose tissue. Outermost zone approximately same width as middle zone and composed of concentric wavy laminae and short radial pillars; laminae follow surface irregularities caused by nodes and interspaces.

DISCUSSION: As far as the writer knows, *B. clarki* is the first beatriceoid stromatoporoid to have sharply deviated from the near-circular transverse outline characteristic of the genus. Three well-defined zones of tissue are present in *B. clarki*, yet Raymond (1914, p. 10) stated that ". . . most descriptions of *B. nodulosa* and *B. (Aulacera) undulata* do not specifically describe the three zones . . ." He (p. 10) went on to point out that ". . . an inspection of the macroscopic character of specimens from Anticosti shows that both an outer or 'sheath' zone and the axial tube are present in well preserved specimens." Raymond mentioned that Parks (1910) had also described a *A. undulata*

TABLE 1. DISTRIBUTION OF SPECIES DESCRIBED FROM NORTHERN HUDSON BAY LOWLAND

	Portage Chute Formation	Surprise Creek Formation	Caution Creek Formation	Chasm Creek Formation	Red Head Rapids Formation
Stromatoporoids					
Beatricea nodulosa	..	X	..	X	..
B. clarki	..	..	..	X	..
Aulacera undulata	..	?	X	X	..
Corals					
Palaeophyllum stokesi	X	..	..	X	..
P. halysitoides	X	..	..	..	..
P. raduguini	..	..	X	X	..
Grewingkia robusta	X	..	..	..	..
Lobocorallium goniophylloides	..	X	..	..	..
L. trilobatum var. major	..	..	X	X	..
Deiracorallium manitobense	..	..	X	X	..
D. manitobense var. churchillense	..	..	..	X	..
D. giganteum	..	..	..	X	..
Bighornia patella	..	..	X	X	..
B. solearis	..	..	..	X	..
B. bottei	..	..	..	X	..
Phaulactis stummi	..	..	..	X	..
Favistella alveolata	X	..	..	X	..
F. alveolata var. stellaris	..	..	..	X	..
Nyctopora(?) foerstei	X	..	..	..	..
N. mackenziei	X	X	..	..	..
Saffordophyllum(?) portagechutense	X	..	..	..	..
Lyopora manitobensis	..	..	X	X	..
L. churchillensis	..	..	..	X	..
Calapoecia anticostiensis	X	X	X	X	..
C. arctica(?)	X	..	..	..	..
C. canadensis var. ungava	..	..	X	X	..
Protrochiscolithus kiaeri	..	..	X	X	..
Plasmopora lambei	X	X	..	..	..
P. pattersoni	X	..	..	..	..
Palaeofavosites alveolaris(?)	..	..	X	X	..
P. prolificus	..	..	..	X	..
P. capax	..	..	X	X	..
P. okulitchi	..	..	..	X	..
Favosites wilsonae	..	..	X	..	..
Catenipora rubra	X	..	X	X	..
C. robusta	X	X	X	X	..
C. stearni	X	..	X	..	..
C. aequabilis	X	X	..	..	..
C. agglomeratiformis	X	..	..	..	..
C. foerstei	..	..	X	..	..
C. sp.	..	..	..	X	..
Manipora amicarum	X	..	X	X	..
M. irregularis	X	..	..	X	..
M. feildeni	X	..	..	..	..
Graptolite					
Desmograptus canadensis	..	..	X	..	..
Gastropods					
Trochonema coxi	X	X	X	X	..
Holopea gigantea	X	..	..	..	..
Liospira parva	..	..	X	..	..
Hormotoma winnipegensis	X	..	..	..	..
Maclurites manitobensis	X	X	..	..	..
M. altus	X	..	..	..	..
M. ungava	X	..	..	..	..
Fusispira gigantea	X	..	..	..	..

TABLE 1—*Continued*

	Portage Chute Formation	Surprise Creek Formation	Caution Creek Formation	Chasm Creek Formation	Red Head Rapids Formation
Cephalopods					
?*Cyclendoceras kindlei*	×	..	..	..	..
C. belli	..	..	×	..	..
Parksoceras lepidodendroides	..	..	×	..	..
Narthecoceras crassisiphonatum	×	×	×	..	..
Kochoceras bailliei	..	..	..	×	..
K. giganteum	..	..	..	×	..
K. sp. I	×	..	..	..	..
K. sp. II	..	..	..	..	×
Huronia septata	..	..	..	×	..
Lambeoceras kronlundi	×	..	..	..	..
L. nudum	..	..	×	..	..
L. landerense	×	..	..	..	..
L. baffinense	×	..	..	..	..
L. walkeri	..	×	..	..	..
Paractinoceras canadense	×	..	..	..	..
P.(?) *churchillense*	..	..	..	×	..
Gorbyoceras giganteum	..	..	..	×	..
Ephippiorthoceras dowlingi	..	..	×	..	..
Whiteavesites winnipegensis	×	..	..	..	..
W. procteri	..	×	..	..	..
Probillingsites harkeri	..	..	×	..	..
Billingsites costulatus	×	..	..	..	..
B. landerensis	×	..	..	..	..
B. borealis	..	..	×	..	..
B. keatingi	..	..	×	..	..
B. canadensis	..	..	×	..	..
Digenuoceras latum	×	..	..	..	..
D. mclearni	..	..	×	..	..
D. okulitchi	..	..	..	×	..
Exomegoceras wyomingense	×	..	..	..	..
Neumatoceras churchillense	×	..	..	..	..
Westonoceras nelsonense	×	..	..	..	..
Winnipegoceras laticurvatum	×	..	..	..	..
W. dowlingi	×	..	..	..	..
W. nelsonense	×	..	..	..	..
W.(?) *contractum*	..	..	×	..	..
W. callahani	..	..	..	×	..
Cyrtogomphoceras turgidum	×	..	..	..	..
C. nutatum	×	..	..	..	..
C. rotundum	×	..	..	..	..
C. baffinense	×	..	..	..	..
C. thompsoni	×	..	..	..	..
C. foerstei	×	..	..	..	..
C. alcocki	×	..	..	..	..
Antiplectoceras shamattawaense	..	..	..	×	..
Fremontoceras sp., cf. *F. loperi*	..	..	..	×	..
Apsidoceras boreale	..	..	..	×	..
A. milleri	..	..	..	×	..
Charactoceras manitobense	×	..	..	..	..
C. laddi	..	..	×	..	..
C. warrenae	..	..	×	..	..
Charactocerina kirki	×	..	..	..	..
C. goodwini	..	..	×	..	..
C. leithi	..	..	..	×	..
Wilsonoceras squawcreekense	×	..	..	..	..
Kinaschukoceras churchillense	..	..	..	×	..

having the three zones. These zones which the latter author described are strikingly similar to those of *B. clarki*. Parks (1910, p. 44) stated:

"This specimen is 75 mm. thick and presents in cross section a series of concentric layers of very different aspect. The inner tube has a radius of only 3 mm. This is surrounded by a ring, 20 mm. thick, of ordinary vesicular tissue with the granular element well developed, but with scarcely a trace of radial pillars. Surrounding this ring is an outer zone, 15 mm. thick, which is fairly well demarked by a sharp line of separation. This outer layer is strikingly different from the middle annulus, being composed of continuous laminae and well marked radial pillars."

Beatricea clarki is probably closest to *B. nodulosa*, for both species have a nodulose outer surface. The three concave sides of *B. clarki* are reminiscent of the outer undulatory surface of *Aulacera undulata*. However, the latter species has numerous undulations, whereas *B. clarki* has only three and also has a nodulose outer layer, as compared with the smooth one of *A. undulata*.

The kind of cameration in the axial zone of *B. clarki* is unknown. The paratype was sectioned, but, although vestiges of cameration could be seen, secondary calcite deposition has destroyed most of its original shape.

The Nelson River specimen has smaller nodes than the holotype, but similar variation is known in *B. nodulosa*, and it is not considered of taxonomic importance.

Genus *Aulacera* Plummer, 1843
Type Species: *Beatricea undulata* Billings, 1857
Aulacera undulata (Billings)

1857 *Beatricea undulata* BILLINGS, Geol. Surv. Canada Rept. of Prog. 1853–1856, p. 344
1865 *Beatricea undulata* Billings. BILLINGS, Canadian Nat. and Geol., New Ser., v. 2, p. 405, figs. 1, 2
1895 *Beatricea undulata* Billings. WHITEAVES, Geol. Surv. Canada Pal. Foss., v. 3, pt. 2, p. 114
1909 *Beatricea undulata* Billings. FOERSTE, Denison Univ. Bull., Jour. Sci. Lab., v. 14, p. 298, Pl. 8, fig. 3
1910 *Beatricea undulata* Billings. PARKS, Univ. Toronto Studies, Geol. Ser., no. 7, p. 43, Pl. 25, figs. 1, 6, 7
1928 *Beatricea (Aulacera) undulata* Billings. TWENHOFEL, Geol. Surv. Canada Mem. 154, p. 105
1943 *Beatricea undulata* Billings. OKULITCH, Trans. Roy. Soc. Canada, v. 37, sec. 4, Pl. 2, fig. 1
1956 *Aulacera undulata* (Billings). LECOMPTE, Treat. Invert. Pal., pt. F, p. 142

OCCURRENCE: One specimen from Member No. 3 of Chasm Creek Formation, Churchill River: locality 25290. Common in same formation on Nelson River: locality 25267. One specimen from beds tentatively referred to Upper Member of Caution Creek Formation, South Knife River: locality 25308 (*see* Chasm Creek Formation)

DISCUSSION: In addition to these specimens a large *Aulacera undulata* was collected from rubble at the mouth of Surprise Creek (locality 25279), Churchill River. This specimen may have been derived either from the Surprise Creek or the Caution Creek Formation, both of which crop out along this creek. A weathered chert nodule attached to the outer surface of the fossil suggests that it may be from the Surprise Creek for chert is rare in the Caution Creek but abundant in the Surprise Creek.

Aulacera undulata occurs in the Vaureal and Ellis Bay formations on Anticosti Island and has been reported from beds of Richmondian age at Lake St. John, Quebec, Lake Huron, and the Ohio Valley. In southern Manitoba it occurs in the Penitentiary and Gunton members of the Stony Mountain Formation.

Class ANTHOZOA Ehrenberg
Order RUGOSA Milne-Edwards and Haime
Family STREPTELASMATIDAE Nicholson
Genus *Palaeophyllum* Billings, 1858
Type Species: *Palaeophyllum rugosum* Billings, 1858

Corallites fasciculate or halysitoid. Where free most of them are circular or oval in transverse section, but where appressed against adjacent corallites, as in halysitoid forms, they tend to be subpolygonal. Septa are simple and of two alternating orders. Corallites have about 20 primary septa which may extend to the center. Most tabulae are horizontal but may be deflected downward at the margin.

Palaeophyllum stokesi (Milne-Edwards and Haime)
(Pl. 6, fig. 6)

1851 *Lithostrotion Stokesi* MILNE-EDWARDS and HAIME, Polyp. Foss. des Terr. Pal., p. 440, Pl. 20, fig. 2
1858 [?] *Palaeophyllum rugosum* BILLINGS, Geol. Surv. Canada Rept., Prog., 1857, p. 168
1897 *Diphyphyllum Stokesi* (Edwards and Haime). WHITEAVES, Geol. Surv. Canada Pal. Foss., v. 3, pt. 3, p. 152, Pl. 17, figs. 5, 5a-b
1899 [?] *Columnaria rugosa* (Billings). LAMBE, Ottawa Nat., v. 12, p. 217
1901 [?] *Columnaria rugosa* (Billings) LAMBE, Geol. Surv. Canada Contr. Canadian Pal., v. 4, pt. 2, p. 101, Pl. 6, figs. 3, 3a-b
1915 *Columnaria (Palaeophyllum) stokesi* (Edwards and Haime). BASSLER, United States Nat. Mus. Bull. 92, v. 1, p. 261
1926 *Columnaria (Palaeophyllum) stokesi* (Edwards and Haime). HUSSEY, Contr. Mus. Geol. Univ. Michigan, v. 2, no. 8, p. 151, Pl. 11, fig. 15
1928 [not] *Columnaria (Palaeophyllum) stokesi* (Edwards and Haime). TROEDSSON, Medd. om Grønland, v. 72, p. 111, Pl. 27, figs. 1a-d
1950 [?] *Palaeophyllum rugosum* Billings. BASSLER, Geol. Soc. America Mem. 44, p. 274, Pl. 18, figs. 15, 16

OCCURRENCE: Common in Member No. 2 of Portage Chute Formation, Churchill and South Knife rivers: nearly all areas of outcrop. Rare in Member No. 1 of Chasm Creek Formation, Churchill River: locality 25283

Hypotype, G.S.C. No. 10372: Member No. 2, Portage Chute Formation, South Knife River, locality 25299

DESCRIPTION: Northern Manitoban corallites nearly circular and when mature have diameter of 6–7 mm. Corallites free or a few in contact, but never exhibit halysitoid pattern. Septa of two orders. Primary septa, from 21 to 23, extend between ½ to ¾ distance to center, with little or no twisting, and axial hollow results. This space in most specimens appears circular in transverse polished section and has diameter between ⅓ and ¼ that of corallite. In some sections it appears almost like an aulos. Secondary septa alternate with major ones, about ⅛ to ¼ their length, and in some corallites obscured by peripheral deposits of stereoplasm.

Tabulae about 0.5 mm apart and flat or slightly undulating in center and bent downwards at margin.

DISCUSSION: *Palaeophyllum stokesi* was first described as a species of *Lithostrotion* by Milne-Edwards and Haime (1851) from the "Carboniferous" of Lake Winnipeg, Manitoba. It has since been assumed that it was collected from strata now known as the Red River Formation. Whiteaves' (1897, p. 152–153) interpretation of the species is much the same as that of the present writer.

As Lambe (1901, p. 101) indicated, *Palaeophyllum stokesi* and the Black Riverian species *P. rugosum* (Billings) may be conspecific. The writer has not examined type material of the latter species from Lake St. John. From the literature, however, the structure of the two species appears very close and the present writer is questionably placing them in synonymy.

In the Lake Winnipeg area *P. stokesi* has been reported from the Red River Formation. Bassler (1950, p. 22) indicated that it also occurs in the overlying Stony Mountain Formation.

Palaeophyllum halysitoides (Wilson)
(Pl. 5, fig. 4)

1926 *Diphyphyllum? halysitoides* WILSON, Geol. Surv. Canada, Geol. Ser. 46, Bull. 44, p. 18, Pl. 2, figs. 8, 9
1928 *Columnaria halysitoides* TROEDSSON, Medd. om Grønland, v. 72, p. 113, Pl. 28, figs. 1–5

OCCURRENCE: Fairly common in Member No. 1 of the Portage Chute Formation, North Knife River: localities 25313, 25314; and in Member No. 2 of this formation, Nelson and Churchill rivers: nearly all areas of outcrop

Hypotype, G.S.C. No. 10370: Member No. 2, Portage Chute Formation, Churchill River, locality 25271

DESCRIPTION: Corallites of northern Manitoban specimens commonly have halysitoid arrangement and range in diameter from 3 to 5 mm; 4 mm corallites most common. Septa of two orders and alternate. In mature corallites, 18–23 primary septa extend nearly to center, and in about half of these there is small axial finely vesicular zone probably caused by intersection of septa with tabulae. Secondary septa very short.

Tabulae 0.5–0.7 mm apart and variable in pattern: majority convex upward. Others flat over most of corallite and sharply deflected downward at margin.

DISCUSSION: When Wilson (1926) erected this species she questionably referred it to *Diphyphyllum*. The present writer thinks it should be referred to *Palaeophyllum* as there is no trace of a dissepimentarium in the type specimen from the Beaverfoot Formation of British Columbia. Among the diagnostic features of the species, Wilson noted the halysitoid arrangement of the corallites and that in each corallite approximately 20 primary septa extend nearly to the center.

Troedsson described from the Cape Calhoun Series of northern Greenland a new species he called *Columnaria halysitoides*. His specimens are better preserved than the Beaverfoot material, and his diagnosis is similar to Wilson's. The present writer is therefore placing Troedsson's *C. halysitoides* in synonymy with Wilson's species.

Palaeophyllum raduguini n. nov.
(Pl. 6, fig. 7)

1936 *Columnaria halysitoides* RADUGUIN, Rec. Geol. West Siberian Reg., no. 35, p. 100, Pl. 2, fig. 12

OCCURRENCE: Rare in Member No. 1 of Caution Creek Formation, Churchill River: locality 25281; and in Members No. 1 and No. 2 of Chasm Creek Formation: localities 25283, 25286, respectively

Hypotype, G.S.C. No. 10371: Member No. 2, Chasm Creek Formation, Churchill River, locality 25286

DESCRIPTION: Churchill River specimens appear very similar to Siberian material described by Raduguin. Most corallites have halysitoid arrangement, and individual diameters range between 2.5 and 3.5 mm. There are 16–18 primary septa in each corallite, which either extend directly to center or unite by two's, three's and four's before reaching it. At center they fuse to form simple axial mass, with little or no vesicular tissue. Secondary septa very short and most obscured by thick deposits of peripheral stereoplasm.

Tabulae about 0.5 mm apart and appear to have same pattern as in *P. halysitoides* (Wilson).

DISCUSSION: Raduguin's description of this species is fairly detailed, but his single illustration unfortunately is very poor. His specific name is preoccupied by Wilson (1926), and the present writer is renaming the species.

A summary of the translation of Raduguin's description is as follows:

The corallites are subcylindrical to cylindrical and are usually joined in a halysitoid pattern. Diameter of mature corallites varies between 3.5 and 4.0 mm. Most primary septa number between 14 and 16 and extend towards the center where they fuse in bunches of 2 or 3 to form a nearly solid mass. The septa are not twisted, and it can be said that a false columella is formed. Secondary septa are very short, generally about 0.2 mm long. Most tabulae are spaced between ⅗ and 1 mm apart and are nearly flat or slightly bent.

Hudson Bay Lowland specimens referred to *P. halysitoides* and *P. raduguini* are quite similar. The difference between the two species is brought out only through study of a large number of corallites.

Genus *Grewingkia* Dybowski, 1873
Type Species: *Clisiophyllum buceros* Eichwald, 1855
Grewingkia robusta (Whiteaves)
(Pl. 8, figs. 1a, b, 2, 3a–f)

1881 *Streptelasma corniculum?* Hall. WHITEAVES, Geol. Surv. Canada Rept. Prog. 1879–1880, p. 57c
1896 *Streptelasma robustum* WHITEAVES, Canadian Rec. Sci., v. 6, p. 391
1897 *Streptelasma robustum* Whiteaves. WHITEAVES, Geol. Surv. Canada Pal. Foss., v. 3, pt. 3, p. 153, Pl. 18, figs. 1, 1a
1901 *Streptelasma robustum* Whiteaves. LAMBE, Geol. Surv. Canada Contr. Canadian Pal., v. 4, pt. 2, p. 109, Pl. 7, fig. 1
1915 *Streptelasma robustum* Whiteaves. BASSLER, United States Nat. Mus. Bull. 92, v. 2, p. 1204
1931 [?] *Streptelasma? arcticum* WILSON, Trans. Roy. Soc. Canada, v. 25, sec. 4, p. 292, Pl. 2, figs. 1–5
1931 [?] cf. *Streptelasma? arcticum* WILSON, Trans. Roy. Soc. Canada, v. 25, sec. 4, p. 293, Pl. 1, figs. 5, 6
1937 [?] *Streptelasma arcticum* Wilson. COX, Geol. Mag., v. 74, no. 1, p. 5, Pl. 1, figs. 6–9
1937 [?] *Streptelasma robustum* Whiteaves. COX, Geol. Mag., v. 74, no. 1, p. 10, Pl. 2, figs. 1–3
1956 *Grewingkia robusta* (Whiteaves). DUNCAN, United States Geol. Surv. Bull. 1021-F, Pl. 21, figs. 4a, 4b

OCCURRENCE: Common in Member No. 1 of Portage Chute Formation, North Knife River: localities 25312, 25313, 25314, 25315; and in Member No. 2 of this formation, Nelson River, Churchill River, South Knife and North Knife rivers: all areas of outcrop

Hypotype, G.S.C. No. 10807, and plastohypotype, G.S.C. No. 10797:   Member No. 2, Portage Chute Formation, Nelson River, locality 25258
Hypotype, G.S.C. No. 10358:   Member No. 2 Portage Chute Formation, Churchill River, locality 25275

DESCRIPTION: In northern Manitoban specimens septa numerous and of two orders. Between 60 and 70 primary septa extend toward center in mature stages and unite to form finely vermiform axial complex, transverse diameter of which in most specimens between ⅛ and ¼ that of corallum. Secondary septa rather short and most obscured by a peripheral stereozone.

Tabulae appear slightly arched in axial region and slope rather steeply downward to join thecal wall. Dissepiments noted by Whiteaves (1896) in this species probably caused by the section intersecting arched tabulae and septa.

DISCUSSION: Most of the primary types of *G. robusta* from the Red River Formation have been lost. The species occurs in the Dog Head and laterally equivalent Selkirk Member of this formation (Fig. 2). The writer has examined and sectioned Selkirk material and found the Portage Chute specimens nearly identical with them. Whiteaves mentioned that some of his specimens were compressed. This "compression" on the Selkirk material examined by the present writer, is expressed by a fairly well-defined, narrowly rounded longitudinal angulation along the convex side of the corallum at the outer end of the cardinal septum. In late maturity the ridge usually disappears, and the transverse outline of the corallum is nearly circular. Angulation of this kind is common in Portage Chute specimens. A few rare individuals have, besides the cardinal angulation, two other very poorly defined longitudinal ridges, each opposite an alar septum. The same shape is shown on the specimen illustrated by Whiteaves (1897, Pl. 18, fig. 1). Cox (1937, p. 10–11) also noted such angulation on his Akpatok Island *G. robusta*. He stated:

"Although some specimens are nearly circular in section, others may be somewhat angulate longitudinally both on the convex side and on those at 90 degrees to it. The cardinal fossula corresponds in position to the first of these sides."

The subject of this angulation on *G. robusta* is discussed more fully under *Lobocorallium*. The present writer is of the opinion that this species evolved, by development of longitudinal furrows between the cardinal and alar ridges, into the Surprise Creek *Lobocorallium goniophylloides* (Teichert).

The Akpatok Island *G. robusta*, described by Cox (1937), does not appear typical of the species in that the axial complex is coarse and consists of anastomosing ends of only a few septa. The Selkirk specimen of *G. robusta* illustrated by Lambe (1901, Pl. 7, fig. 1) shows the complex to be finely vermiform. Portage Chute and Selkirk specimens examined by the writer also have the latter type of complex.

The primary and secondary types of *Streptelasma arcticum* Wilson from Baffin Island and Akpatok Island, respectively, should be re-examined. The internal structures of this species, illustrated by Cox (1937), are very similar to those specimens of *G. robusta* studied by the present writer, and illustrated by Lambe (1901, Pl. 7, fig. 1). Cox, in his synonymy, however, did not consider that the specimen illustrated by Lambe was *G. robusta*, but gave no discussion of his reasons for this assumption. Since the Selkirk specimens of *G. robusta* examined by the present writer are very similar, in transverse section, to Lambe's drawing of the specimen it is thought that a finely vermiform axial complex is characteristic of the species.

Specimens probably referable to *G. robusta* have been described from various localities in the Arctic by Troedsson (1928), Roy (1941), and Miller, Youngquist, and Collinson (1954). These records are not included in the synonymy because illustrations of longitudinal and transverse sections, which would permit definite identification, are wanting. Many of these specimens have a well-defined angulation, and it may well be that future work will show this feature to be characteristic of the species.

Genus Lobocorallium nov.
Type Species: Streptelasma rusticum var. trilobatum Whiteaves, 1895

DIAGNOSIS: This genus contains solitary corals in which two broad longitudinal furrows, one on each cardinal wall, give the corallum a trilobate appearance. The outer parts of the three lobes correspond to the cardinal septum and each of the two alar septa, respectively. The cardinal lobe on all specimens is on the longitudinally convex side of the corallum and is generally more lobate than the others. Furrows develop early and deepen and widen throughout maturity.

Septa are strongly dilated, numerous, of two orders, and extend to the center. A cardinal fossula may be present.

Tabulae are numerous, approximately parallel, and strongly arched.

DISCUSSION: The generic name refers to the lobed appearance of the corallum.

This diagnosis is based on the holotype and topotypes of *L. trilobatum* from southern Manitoba. These specimens are small, and it is thought that they are immature. Numerous large trilobate corals occur in the Churchill River Group of the Lowland. Besides their size they differ from those in southern Manitoba in having an axial complex which develops during late youth or early maturity. Early growth structures of the two, however, are very similar. Later work may show that the generic diagnosis should be revised to include those forms with the axial complex. Until it can be proven that the Churchill River Group corals are conspecific with *L. trilobatum*, however, they will be referred to *L. trilobatum* var. *major* nov.

Species included in this genus are thought to form a direct evolutionary series tending toward increased trilobation of the corallum. The ancestral species is considered to be the Portage Chute *Grewingkia robusta* (Whiteaves). This species appears to have rapidly evolved into the Surprise Creek *Lobocorallium goniophylloides* (Teichert) which in turn probably gave rise to *L. trilobatum* var. *major* of the overlying Churchill River Group.

Many Portage Chute specimens of *Grewingkia robusta* have a well-defined longitudinal angulation along the convex (cardinal) side of the corallum. *Lobocorallium goniophylloides* appears in the overlying Surprise Creek Formation and, except for more closely spaced and strongly arched tabulae, its internal structures are very similar to those of *G. robusta*. The cardinal side of *L. goniophylloides*, in young stages, is angulated (as in mature *G. robusta*) but, in early maturity, two furrows appear and the cardinal angulation becomes narrowly rounded and weakly lobate. *Lobocorallium goniophylloides* apparently gave rise to *L. trilobatum* var. *major* in which furrows are deeper, trilobation more marked, cardinal lobe broader and more rounded than on the former. *Lobocorallium trilobatum* var. *major* appears first in the basal beds of the Caution Creek Formation and ranges through this and the lower three members of the overlying Chasm Creek Formation without apparent change.

This evolutionary sequence was first commented upon by Kirk (1925, p. 446). He suggested that

L. haysi (which is probably conspecific with *L. goniophylloides*) may have given rise to *L. trilobatum* (*s.s.*).

Lobocorallium haysi goniophylloides (Teichert)
(Pl. 9, figs. 1a, b, 2a–c, 3a, b, 4)

1865 [?] *Zaphrentis Haysii* MEEK, American Jour. Sci. Arts, Ser. 2, v. 40, p. 32
1925 [?] *Streptelasma haysii* (Meek). KIRK, American Jour. Sci., Ser. 5, v. 10, p. 445
1929 [?] *Streptelasma haysii* (Meek). LADD, Iowa Geol. Surv. Ann. Rept., v. 34, p. 396, Pl. 4, figs. 1–5
1937 [?] *Streptelasma foerstei* Troedsson. COX, Geol. Mag., v. 74, no. 1, p. 6, Pl. 1, figs. 10–16
1937 [?] *Streptelasma haysii* (Meek). COX, Geol. Mag., v. 74, no. 1, p. 8, Pl. 2, figs. 4a, b
1937 *Streptelasma goniophylloides* TEICHERT, Rept. Fifth Thule Exped. 1921–1924, v. 1, no. 5, p. 49, Pl. 3, figs. 5–11
1941 [?] *Streptelasma* sp. III ROY, Field Mus. Nat. Hist. Geol. Mem., v. 2, p. 69, figs. 34e, f
1954 [?] *Streptelasma* spp. MILLER, YOUNGQUIST, and COLLINSON [*partim*], Geol. Soc. America Mem. 62, p. 10, Pl. 7, figs. 1, 2

OCCURRENCE: Surprise Creek Formation: rare in Member No. 1, Churchill River: locality 25272; and in the Lower Member on Nelson River: localities 25260, 25261

Hypotypes, G.S.C. Nos. 10793 and 10795 (and plastohypotype 10794): locality 25272

DESCRIPTION: Hudson Bay Lowland specimens referred to this species rather weakly trilobate and can attain maximum height of 130 mm. Poorly defined, shallow longitudinal furrow present along thecal wall of each cardinal quadrant. Cardinal lobe in most specimens subangular or narrowly rounded in transverse outline. Furrows of most specimens disappear in ephebic stages, and corallum has subquadrangular transverse outline.

Number and arrangement of septa and development of axial complex similar to that of northern Manitoba *L. trilobatum* var. *major*. Transverse outline of complex less clearly trilobate than in that species.

Tabulae strongly and uniformly arched over corallum.

Diameters (in mm) and number of septa in hypotypes follow. Distance of each section from apex measured along cardinal lobe.

Hypotype	Cardinal-counter diameter	Alar diameter	Number of primary septa	Width of axial complex	Height above apex
10793a	17	16	49	0	9
10793b	20	21	56	4	15
10793c	26	26	66	8	21
10795 Polished Sections					
1	30	30	69	10	25
2	48	46	87	20	65 (est.)

DISCUSSION: Lowland specimens are almost identical with the holotype of *Streptelasma goniophylloides* Teichert from Mount Nautilus, Baffin Island. In the writer's opinion the similarly trilobate, earlier-described *S. haysi* is conspecific. Until internal structures of the lectotype of the latter species have been described, it is considered best to refer present material to *L. goniophylloides* rather than *S. haysi* (*s.s.*).

Lobocorallium trilobatum var. *major* nov.
(Pl. 5, fig. 1; Pl. 8, fig. 4; Pl. 10, figs. 1, 2a–h)

1895 [?] *Streptelasma rusticum* var. *trilobatum* WHITEAVES, Geol. Surv. Canada Pal. Foss., v. 3, pt. 2, p. 113
1928 [?] *Zaphrentis vaurealensis* TWENHOFEL, Geol. Surv. Canada Mem. 154, p. 116, Pl. 3, fig. 1
1928 [?] *Streptelasma robustum* Whiteaves [*partim*]. TROEDSSON, Medd. om. Grønland, v. 72, p. 108, Pl. 25, fig. 2
1928 [?] *Streptelasma robustum* var. *amplum* TROEDSSON, Medd. om. Grønland, v. 72, p. 108, Pl. 26, figs. 1–4

1928 [?] *Streptelasma foerstei* TROEDSSON, Medd. om. Grønland, v. 72, p. 109, Pl. 25, figs. 1, 3; Pl. 26, fig. 5
1937 [*non* ?] *Streptelasma foerstei* Troedsson. Cox, Geol. Mag., v. 74, no. 1, p. 6, Pl. 1, figs. 10–16
1956 [?] *Streptelasma trilobatum* (Whiteaves). DUNCAN, United States Geol. Surv. Bull. 1021-F, Pl. 21, figs. 3a, b
1959b *Streptelasma trilobatum* (Whiteaves) var. NELSON, Jour. Alberta Soc. Pet. Geol., v. 7, no. 3, Pl. 3, figs. 3a, b

OCCURRENCE: Common in Members No. 1 and No. 3 of the Caution Creek Formation, Churchill River: all areas of outcrop; and in the Upper Member of this formation, South Knife River; all areas of outcrop west of the northward bend of this river. Common in the Chasm Creek Formation, Nelson River: all areas of outcrop; and in Members No. 1, No. 2 and No. 3 of this formation, Churchill River: all areas of outcrop

Holotype, G.S.C. No. 10796: Member No. 3, Chasm Creek Formation, Churchill River, locality 25290
Paratype, G.S.C. Nos. 10811, 10356: Member No. 1, Chasm Creek Formation, Churchill River, locality 25281

DESCRIPTION: Northern Lowland specimens referred to this variety markedly trilobate, and most large; they attain maximum length of 230 mm. Broad well-developed furrow present on each cardinal quadrant, and cardinal lobe more or less broadly rounded in transverse profile. Trilobation starts fairly early and continues throughout maturity. In some specimens degree of trilobation lessens during old age so that transverse profile subcircular. Most specimens have shape similar to that of plastoholotype No. 10797 (Pl. 10, fig. 1). Some, however, have markedly transversely elongated cardinal lobe and trochoid outline as in *Streptelasma robustum* var. *amplum* Troedsson. Rare individuals have elongated alar lobes and rather short cardinal lobe. Internal structures of these variously shaped specimens similar, and thought that they belong in same species. Weathered specimens show calyx to be fairly deep, and subconical spongious boss formed by axial complex.

Septa numerous, closely spaced and of two orders. Primary septa strongly dilated in youth and extend directly to center with little or no twisting in axial region. Later they anastomose and form axial complex consisting of few thickened ends of septa. This complex becomes wider and finely vermiform or subreticulate during later maturity and old age and has subtrilobate outline. Most secondary septa obscured by thick peripheral stereozone. Cardinal septum aborted in mature and later stages and forms prominent fossula.

Tabulae closely spaced. In youth and early maturity strongly and rather uniformly arched over width of corallum. Later tend to be more gently inclined toward periphery but arched in axial region.

Holotype No. 10796, largest and most complete specimen collected, has been cast in plaster (plastoholotype No. 10797) and original cut into numerous transverse sections. Following details of its structure typical of most Lowland specimens referred to variety.

Thin sections (hypotype No. 10796)	Cardinal-counter diameter	Alar diameter	Number of primary septa	Alar width of axial complex
10796a	14	13	36 (est.)	Absent
10796b	19	20	46	2
10796c	21	23	48	5
10796d	29	31	54	12
10796e	32	32 (est.)	58	14
10796f	32	34	64	14
10796g	35	36 (est.)	70	13
10796h	38	40	74	16
10796i	38	42	76	20
10796j	43	44	80	20
10796k	47	46	84	20
10796l	51 (est.)	50	86	21
10796m	54	52 (est.)	90	22

DISCUSSION: *Lobocorallium trilobatum* (*s.s.*) was originally described from southern Manitoba in beds now called the Stony Mountain Shale Member of the Stony Mountain Formation. Specimens from this member, examined by the present writer are all small and lack an axial complex. In the largest specimen sectioned, at 23 mm from the apex, the septa showed a tendency to twist slightly at the center. Specimens of the Hudson Bay variety, are nearly always large, lack an axial complex in early growth stages but later form a well-developed one. The writer is of the opinion that the Hudson Bay specimens are either a large or a mature variety of *L. trilobatum*. Those in southern Manitoba may be small because of environmental conditions. The same size difference was found to hold for most of the other coral species common to the two areas. If a large topotype of *L. trilobatum* can be found and sectioned for axial details conspecific relations might be demonstrated. No axial complex, however, is shown in the large Bighorn specimen of *L. trilobatum* diagrammatically illustrated by Duncan (1956, Pl. 21, figs. 3a, b).

The large trilobate Greenland species *Streptelasma foerstei* Troedsson may be conspecific with the Hudson Bay specimens. Troedsson did not describe internal structures of his specimens but their exterior is markedly trilobate. The specimens of *S. foerstei* from the same area, described and sectioned by Cox, however, do not appear markedly trilobate, and their transverse outline is very similar to those which the writer calls *L. goniophylloides*.

Zaphrenthis vaurealensis Twenhofel, from the Vaureal Formation of Anticosti Island, may be related to *L. trilobatum* var. *major*. Twenhofel's (1928) illustration suggests that only a longitudinal half of the corallum is preserved. He stated that "On one side is a groove about 8 to 20 mm. wide, which extends from the tip to the top of the calyx following the curvature of the corallum." Tabulae, however, were stated to be absent in the lower part of the corallum.

Genus *Deiracorallium* nov.

Type Species: *Deiracorallium manitobense* nov.

DIAGNOSIS: Solitary corals in which the longitudinally convex side of the thecal wall is markedly angulated, the angulation corresponding to the outer extremity of the cardinal septum. The calyx is fairly deep.

Septa are numerous, simple, show excellent tetrameral symmetry, and join at the center of the corallum without twisting. A well-defined cardinal fossula is present.

Tabulae are closely spaced and nearly flat or gently convex upward.

DISCUSSION: The generic name refers to the presence of the ridge along the thecal wall.

Three distinct kinds of *Deiracorallium* are recognized in northern Manitoba. The most common species is *D. manitobense* which occurs in the Caution Creek and Member No. 1 of the Chasm Creek Formation. It is characterized by having a small size, acute angulation, and simple septa without an axial complex. The second kind, represented by a single specimen from Member No. 1 of the Chasm Creek, is here called *D. manitobense* var. *churchillense*. It is small, distinctly curved, and has a more rounded angulation than the first species. It may be an aberrant specimen of *D. manitobense*. The third, called *D. giganteum*, occurs in Member No. 2 of the Chasm Creek Formation. The corallum is large, has a rounded angulation, and septa twist slightly before reaching the center. *Deiracorallium manitobense* by an increase in size and decrease in angulation may have given rise to the stratigraphically higher *D. giganteum*.

The transverse outline of *Deiracorallium* is rather similar to that of neanic stages of *Lobocorallium*, and it is possible that the two may be genetically related. Both have a more or less angulated longitudinally convex side and a fairly prominent fossula, the outer end of which corresponds to the angulation or lobe. Internal structures, however, are not similar, and no transitional forms have been found.

Deiracorallium manitobense sp. nov.

(Pl. 13, figs. 1, 2a, b)

1943 *Streptelasma trilobatum* (Whiteaves) [*partim*]. OKULITCH, Trans. Roy. Soc. Canada, v. 37, sec. 4, p. 61

1959b "*Streptelasma angulatum* (Billings)". NELSON, Jour. Alberta Soc. Pet. Geol., v. 7, no. 3, Pl. 4, figs. 2a, b

OCCURRENCE: Common in Member No. 1 of Caution Creek Formation, Churchill River: all areas of outcrop; and in Member No. 1 of Chasm Creek Formation: locality 25281. Fairly common in Upper Member of Caution Creek Formation, South Knife River: nearly all areas of outcrop west of the northward bend of the river

Holotype, G.S.C. No. 10844: Member No. 1, Caution Creek Formation, Churchill River, locality 25277
Paratypes, G.S.C. Nos. 10355, 10846: Member No. 1 Caution Creek Formation, Churchill River, localities 25282, 25280, respectively
Paratype, G.S.C. No. 10845: Member No. 1, Chasm Creek Formation, Churchill River, locality 25281

DESCRIPTION: Specimens referred to this species generally attain length of about 15 mm, although some reach maximum of 20 mm. Calyx deep, nearly half length of shell, and approximately V-shaped in longitudinal alar profile.

Septa well defined and of two orders. Primary septa extend directly to center without twisting. Secondary septa very short. Cardinal fossula well developed, situated on convex side of corallum, and apparently present in early growth stages.

Most tabulae obscured by sclerenchyme. Paratype No. 10355, however, has well-developed simple and arched tabulae. They are about 0.5 mm apart, arched in lower part of corallum and about 0.25 mm distant and very gently convex upward or flat in upper part.

Measurements (in mm) made on types as follows. Dimensions taken at top of calyx.

Type	Cardinal-counter diameter	Alar diameter	Number of primary septa
10844	15.5	12	33
10845	13	12	34
10846	17	14	35

DISCUSSION: Okulitch (1943) identified three specimens from the Stony Mountain Shale Member of the Stony Mountain Formation which he referred to the young of *Streptelasma trilobatum* (Whiteaves). These specimens are now in the Geological Survey of Canada collections (lot No. 3980). The smallest specimen appears to be a *D. manitobense*. In addition the writer has found this species to be fairly common in the Geological Survey of Canada collection (lot No. 6841) of corals from the Stony Mountain Shale.

Very probably the Beaverfoot *Streptelasma prolongatum* Wilson belongs in *Deiracorallium*. The species is very similar to *D. manitobense* but differs in being larger and less markedly angulated.

Deiracorallium manitobense may be conspecific with *Streptelasma angulatum* (Billings) from the English Head and Vaureal formations of Anticosti Island. Externally the holotype of the latter is very similar to specimens of *D. manitobense*. Twenhofel (1928, p. 111), however, mentioned that the angulation of *S. angulatum* was not always in the same position, and that septa united by two's and three's before reaching the center. No tabulae are preserved in the holotype of *S. angulatum*. The transverse section of this specimen given by Cox (1937) is across the counter side of the corallum so that it is not known if a cardinal fossula is present.

Deiracorallium manitobense var. *churchillense* nov.
(Pl. 13, figs. 3a, b)

OCCURRENCE: One specimen (holotype, G.S.C. No. 10847) from Member No. 1 of Chasm Creek Formation, Churchill River: locality 25281

DESCRIPTION: Variety represented by well-preserved silicified specimen about 9 mm high. Corallum expands rapidly and almost patellate in outline. Cardinal-counter and alar diameters at top of calyx 11 mm and 10 mm respectively. Longitudinal convex side angulated, but ridge more rounded and not so distinct as in *D. angulatum*.

Approximately 36 primary septa present and have same arrangement as in *D. manitobense*.

Deiracorallium giganteum sp. nov.
(Pl. 13, figs. 4a, b, 5, 6a–c)

OCCURRENCE: Two specimens from Member No. 2 of Chasm Creek Formation, Churchill River: localities 25283, 25285

Holotype, G.S.C. No. 10848a-c (thin sections): locality 25285
Paratype, G.S.C. No. 10850: locality 25283

DESCRIPTION: Species based on two well-preserved specimens of which plaster casts (plastoholotype, G.S.C. No. 10849; plastoparatype, G.S.C. No. 10851) have been made.

Both holotype and paratype about 43 mm high. Holotype has cardinal-counter and alar diameters of 33 mm and 26 mm (estimated), respectively, at top of calyx. Paratype has corresponding measurements of 39 mm and 31 mm. Both very similar in outline. Turbinate along extremities of cardinal and counter septa and symmetrical along extremities of alars, rapidly expanding in neanic stages, but decreasing in maturity. Depth of calyx less than half height of corallum.

Primary septa strongly dilated in younger growth stages, and extend directly to center. In later stages septa more discrete and tend to twist and join before reaching center. Secondary septa obscured by peripheral stereozone, width of which about equal to ⅛ diameter of corallite at any one position. Fossula narrow and does not form until late maturity.

Tabulae present, but pattern not known.

Three transverse serial thin sections have been made of holotype and measurements on them of diameter (in mm), and septal counts given below. Distance of each section from apex measured along convex (angulated) side of thecal wall. Estimated measurements indicated.

Holotype (thin section)	Cardinal-counter diameter	Alar diameter	Number of primary septa	Height above apex
10848a	15	13	42	10
10848b	23	20	58	18
10848c	28 (est.)	26 (est.)	60	26

DISCUSSION: *Deiracorallium giganteum* differs from *D. manitobense* in its much larger size and more broadly rounded cardinal angulation. It appears very close to the Kinnikinic quartzite specimen identified by Duncan (1956, Pl. 22, figs. 2a, 2b) as *Streptelasma* aff. *S. prolongatum* Wilson.

Genus *Bighornia* Duncan, 1957
Type Species: *Bighornia parva* Duncan, 1957

The writer is including in this genus solitary tetracorals in which the thecal wall in young stages is typically elongated and flattened parallel to the plane of the alar septa and produces in most specimens a transverse alar diameter greater than that of the cardinal counter. This elongation may be expressed as a calceoloid flattening along the longitudinally convex (counter) side of the corallum as in *B. patella* (Wilson) and *B. parva* Duncan; the concave (cardinal) side as in *B. solearis* (Ladd); or as a spoon-shaped depression on the concave side as in *B. bottei* sp. nov. Most coralla which have the calceoloid flattening along the convex side have an acutely pointed apex; all of those with a flattening or depression on the concave side have a broad shovel-like apex. Most mature and old-age transverse outlines are subcircular or subelliptical. The calyx is relatively deep, flat-bottomed, and has a palicolumella projecting as a boss.

Septa are numerous and of two orders. Primary septa extend toward the center and may or may not form a small vesicular axial complex. A well-developed cardinal fossula is present in mature stages and in most specimens is slightly enlarged or lobate at its inner end. It is situated along the longitudinally *concave* side of the corallum. A very well developed palicolumella, in the plane of the cardinal-counter septa, is present and is, apparently, formed as an elongation and thickening of the inner end of the counter septum. It is solid, rarely vesicular.

Duncan (1957) has given an excellent discussion of this genus and its probable species. In the present area three species are recognized. In order of their stratigraphic appearance they are *B. patella* (Wilson), *B. solearis* (Ladd), and *B. bottei* sp. nov. The last two appear approximately at the same horizon. *Bighornia patella* is distinguished by its relatively small size, pronounced calceoloid flattening along the convex (counter) side of the corallum, and acutely pointed apex. It appears first in Member No. 1 of the Caution Creek Formation and ranges into Member No. 1 of the Chasm Creek Formation. *Bighornia solearis* occurs in the latter member and is represented in the collections by a single specimen. It is distinguished by being slightly larger than *B. patella* and by having only a feebly developed flattening on the convex side. On the opposite (cardinal) side, however, there is a pronounced flattening near the apex, and the apex is transversely elongated in an alar direction. *Bighornia bottei* also appears in Member No. 1 of the Chasm Creek Formation but is most abundant in Members Nos. 2 and 3. It is recognized by its larger size, apex markedly transversely elongated in an alar direction and a well-developed proximal spoon-shaped depression on the cardinal side. The counter side in most specimens is rounded so that a transverse section of the corallum near the apex has a subcrescentic outline. It is thought that *B. patella* evolved into *B. bottei* by an increase in size, development of a distal spoon-shaped depression with consequent extended alar elongation of the apex, and a nearly complete loss of the counter-calceoloid flattening. *Bighornia solearis* may be a transitional species.

Ancestors of *Bighornia* may be such species as *Lindstromia whiteavesi* Foerste from the Ottawa Formation of Ontario (Wilson, 1948) or perhaps *Streptelasma holtedahli* Hill from the Middle Ordovician of Norway (Hill, 1953). Both are characterized by a calceoloid flattening, indistinct fossula, and palicolumella.

Bighornia patella (Wilson)

(Pl. 11, figs. 1a–c, 2, 3a–d)

1926 *Streptelasma patellum* Wilson. Geol. Surv. Canada Bull., 44, Geol. Ser. 46, p. 13, Pl. 2, fig. 1
1928 [?] *Streptelasma* aff. *breve* (Ulrich) Winchell and Schuchert. TROEDSSON, Medd. om Grønland, v. 72, p. 109, Pl. 26, figs. 6, 7
1937 [?] *?Holophragma scheii* Cox, Geol. Mag., v. 74, no. 1, p. 15, Pl. 2, figs. 14–16
1943 *Holophragma anticonvexa* OKULITCH, Trans. Roy. Soc. Canada, v. 37, sec. 4, p. 68, Pl. 1, figs. 11, 12
1959b *Bighornia patella* (Wilson). NELSON, Jour. Alberta Soc. Pet. Geol., v. 7, no. 3, Pl. 4, figs. 1a–d

OCCURRENCE: Abundant in Members No. 1 and No. 3 of Caution Creek Formation, and in Member No. 1 of Chasm Creek Formation, Churchill River: all areas of outcrop. In the last member it is rather rare in the upper 11 feet at localities 25283 and 25284. Common in Upper Member of Caution Creek Formation, South Knife River: nearly all areas of outcrop west of sharp northward bend of river

Hypotype, G.S.C. No. 10872: Member No. 1 Caution Creek Formation, Churchill River, locality 25277
Hypotypes, G.S.C. No. 10873, 10874:   Member No. 1, Chasm Creek Formation, Churchill River, locality 25281

DESCRIPTION: Numerous well-preserved specimens of this species collected and show internal structures much more clearly than previously illustrated forms.

Most specimens about same size as those from Stony Mountain Formation of southern Manitoba, although some attain length of 24 mm or more and have corresponding transverse diameters in plane of cardinal-counter and alar septa of 15 mm and 17 mm, respectively. They have calceoloid flattening along longitudinally convex side of corallum, most prominent in young stages. Apex acutely pointed. Calyx deep and flat-bottomed; its depth a little less than half height of corallum.

Septa numerous and of two orders. Primary septa have good tetrameral symmetry, extend from periphery to axial region where they fuse, most with a little twisting, and join platelike palicolumella which projects 2–3 mm above floor of calyx. Cardinal septum aborted in mature stages and forms prominent fossula. Latter tends to be slightly swollen at inner end and partially surrounds boss. Secondary septa short and alternate with primary septa.

Tabulae probably present, but pattern not known.

Measurements (in mm) of length, corresponding transverse cardinal-counter and alar diameters at top of corallum, and septal counts made on hypotypes listed as follows (estimated dimensions indicated):

Hypotype, no.	Length	Cardinal-counter diameter	Alar diameter	Number of primary septa
10872	14	12	13	34
10873	20	15	17	34
10874	24 (est.)	15	17	39

DISCUSSION: In the writer's opinion *Bighornia patella* (Wilson), *B. anticonvexa* (Okulitch), and possibly *B. parva* are conspecific. Some specimens of *B. anticonvexa* from the Stony Mountain Shale Member of southern Manitoba attain a greater length than the holotype and accordingly have a larger number of septa. The largest specimen examined has a length of 22 mm and 35 major septa. The holotype of *B. patella*, from the Beaverfoot of British Columbia, is poorly preserved. It has an estimated length of 25 mm and cardinal-counter and alar diameters of 17 mm and 18 mm, respectively. About 43 major septa are present. The general appearance of the corallum is very similar to that of the Manitoban specimens. The greater number of septa appears to be an expression of its greater length. It differs from the Bighorn holotype of *B. parva* in having fewer septa per mm. The latter has a length of 17 mm and 46 primary septa.

In Manitoba, *Bighornia patella* appears to be diagnostic of strata correlating with the lower part of the Stony Mountain Formation, *i.e.* Stony Mountain Shale and Penitentiary members.

Bighornia solearis (Ladd)
(Pl. 11, figs. 4a–d)

1929 *Lindstromia solearis* LADD, Iowa Geol. Surv. Ann. Rept., v. 34, p. 397, Pl. 4, figs. 6–12

OCCURRENCE: One specimen (hypotype, G.S.C. No. 10870) from Member No. 1 of Chasm Creek Formation, Churchill River: locality 25281

DESCRIPTION: Hypotype well-preserved silicified individual, almost identical with paratype figured by Ladd (1929, Pl. 4, figs. 9–11). It is about 20 mm high and has corresponding transverse cardinal-counter and alar diameters, at top of calyx, of 17 mm and 19 mm, respectively. Apex flattened in plane of alars, but only very feebly developed depression on cardinal side. In alar profile apex trough-shaped, about 8 mm wide at base, compared with cardinal-counter diameter, at this position, of about 4 mm. Calyx deep, about half length of the corallum, and flat-bottomed. Very well developed platelike palicolumella extends for about 6 mm above bottom of calyx.

Primary septa numerous: near top of corallum approximately 46 extend toward center. Cardinal fossula well developed and slightly bilobed at inner end. It is not, however, so well developed as in *B. bottei* sp. nov.

DISCUSSION: As mentioned in the discussion of the genus *Bighornia*, *B. solearis* is thought to be transitional between *B. patella* and *B. bottei*, because it has some characteristics of both. It retains the small size of the former, but an examination of its apex shows that it is more like *B. bottei*. The apex has a broad, flat troughlike shape like that of *B. bottei*, but is neither so wide nor is the spoon-shaped depression so well developed.

The primary types of *B. solearis* are from the Fort Atkinson Member of the Maquoketa Formation, Iowa.

Bighornia bottei sp. nov.
(Pl. 5, fig. 6; Pl. 9, figs. 5, 6a–d; Pl. 11, figs. 5a, b, 6a–c, 7, 8; Pl. 12, figs. 1, 2a–g, 3a, b, 4a–c)

1959b *Bighornia* sp. NELSON, Jour. Alberta Soc. Pet. Geol., v. 7, no. 3, Pl. 4, figs. 3a-d

OCCURRENCE: Common in Members No. 1, No. 2, and No. 3 of Chasm Creek Formation, Churchill River: all areas of outcrop. Three specimens are from Chasm Creek Formation, Nelson River: locality 25269

Holotype, G.S.C. No. 10898⎫ Member No. 3, Chasm Creek Formation, Churchill River, locality
Paratype, G.S.C. No. 10875⎭   25290

Paratype, G.S.C. No. 10877: Member No. 2, Chasm Creek Formation, Churchill River, locality 25286

Paratype, G.S.C. No. 10881: Member No. 1, Chasm Creek Formation, Churchill River, locality 25283

Paratypes, G.S.C. No. 10882, 10883: Member No. 1, Chasm Creek Formation, Churchill River, locality 25281

Paratype, G.S.C. No. 10879: Chasm Creek Formation, Nelson River: locality 25269

DESCRIPTION: Plaster casts have been made of holotype No. 10898 (plastoholotype No. 10899), paratype No. 10875 (plastoparatype No. 10876), paratype No. 10877 (plastoparatype No. 10878) and paratype No. 10879 (plastoparatype No. 10880). Serial thin sections have been made of original specimens.

Most specimens have length about 50 mm, although largest (paratype No. 10879) has 80 mm, with corresponding cardinal-counter and alar diameters at top of calyx of 46 mm and 40 mm, respectively. Apex strongly flattened approximately parallel to plane of alar septa, and in most has well-defined hollow or spoon-shaped depression on cardinal side.[1] Counter side, in transverse outline, broadly rounded during all growth stages. Thus, most sections taken near base of corallum have crescent-shaped outline. In mature growth stages, corallum has nearly circular transverse outline. Width of trough-shaped apex, measured in alar plane, about 15 mm. Calyx deep, about half height of corallum, and flat-bottomed. Very prominent palicolumella, in plane of cardinal-counter septa, protrudes 5–10 mm above floor of calyx. In most specimens it appears solid, but in paratype No. 10883 is vesicular.

Septa numerous and strongly dilated in early growth stages. Where corallum strongly compressed, near apex, primary septa short and extend inward from periphery fusing along line (in transverse section) in plane of alars giving nearly bilateral symmetry along cardinal-counter plane. Most primary septa added early, and typically little increase in number after about 12 mm above apex. This near constancy in numbers starts just about where cardinal fossula first forms. Maximum number of primary septa about 50, although some specimens have 64. These septa have nearly radial symmetry in mature stages and because of their near-numerical constancy become progressively farther apart distally. They extend toward center, and many fuse before reaching it and form rather obscure axial complex. In center of complex there is some amalgamation with inner end of counter septum to form palicolumella. Cardinal fossula very prominent and dilated or bilobed at inner end. Secondary septa obscured by peripheral stereozone, width of which about ⅛ that of corallum.

Tabulae appear abundant and closely spaced; convex upward on either side of palicolumella and slope downward toward periphery.

Counts of primary septa and measurements (in mm) on thin sections and polished sections given in the accompanying listing. Height of section above apex measured along cardinal side of corallum. Asterisk placed where cardinal fossula first appears. Estimated measurements indicated.

Type	Cardinal-counter diameter	Alar diameter	Number of primary septa	Approximate height of section above apex
Holotype No. 10898				
Thin section No.				
10898a	6	16	36	5
10898b	12	20	38	12
*10898c	18	24	40	16
10898d	24	26	45	21
10898e	28	31	46	28
10898f	29	33	46	33
10898g	31 (est.)	37	46	36
Paratype No. 10875				
Thin section No.				
10875a	7	17	36 (est.)	6
10875b	14	23	46 (est.)	11
*10875c	23	26	48	17

---

[1] Because this side in most specimens is not longitudinally concave as in *B. patella* or *B. solearis* but more nearly straight or slightly convex, it will be referred to hereafter as the "cardinal side".

Type	Cardinal-counter diameter	Alar diameter	Number of primary septa	Approximate height of section above apex
Paratype No. 10877				
Thin section No.				
10877a	12	21	49	7
10877b	20	25	51	13
*10877c	27	28	51	20
Paratype No. 10879				
Thin section No.				
10879a	10	17	42–44	5
*10879b	17	22	48 (est.)	12
10879c	22	24	48	18
10879d	27	27 (est.)	48	25
10879e	37	38 (est.)	50	37
10879f	39	40	51	43
10879g	43	43	51	49
10879h	44	46	51	55
Paratype No. 10881	32	31	60	25–30 (est.)
Polished sections	48	46	64	65–70
Paratype No. 10882	23	30	55	20 (est.)
Polished sections	42	41	57	42 (est.)
Paratype No. 10883	17	26	51–52	14
	36 (est.)	39	57	35 (est.)

DISCUSSION: *Bighornia bottei* is named in honor of Mr. Barford Botte, technician for the Geological Survey of Canada.

The species is represented by numerous individuals showing great variation in shape and size. It has been difficult trying to recognize differences in outer form which would be of specific rank. By studying numerous thin and polished sections, however, the writer has concluded that any differences that exist among the specimens are probably individual variations.

Bighornia bottei is most abundant in Members No. 2 and No. 3 of the Chasm Creek Formation, and is, apparently, diagnostic of these units.

Family HALLIIDAE
Genus *Phaulactis* Ryder, 1926
Type Species: *Phaulactis cyathophylloides* Ryder, 1926
Phaulactis stummi sp. nov.
(Pl. 13, figs. 7, 8a–d, 9–12)

OCCURRENCE: Common in Member No. 3 of Chasm Creek Formation, Churchill River: locality 25290

Holotype G.S.C. No. 10862
Paratypes, G.S.C. Nos. 10863, 10379, 10806, 10900

DESCRIPTION: Corallum moderate size, attaining height of nearly 70 mm; corresponding transverse diameter about 35 mm at top of calyx. Most exteriors strongly annulated. Longitudinal septal ridges generally present, and run length of corallum. Calyx depth about 15 mm in corallum about 70 mm high. Its sides nearly vertical, and floor flat.

Primary septa extend from periphery toward center where they tend to unite by two's, three's and four's, and intertwine to form narrow vermiform axial complex. Secondary septa alternate with primary septa, often difficult to distinguish because of restriction to narrow peripheral dissepimentarium. In mature growth stages prominent fossula present, formed by aborted cardinal septum. This fossula tends to be slightly bulbous at inner end.

In longitudinal sections of neanic stages peripheral dissepimentarium obscure, and tabulae relatively widely spaced and more or less discontinuous. In mature stages dissepimentarium prominent, 2–4 mm wide, and consists of small but variably sized, proximally to near-vertically inclined dissepiments. Central tabularium well developed, and tabulae continuous or discontinuous with latter type tending to form rather open vesicular pattern. Continuous tabulae tend to be convex upward on both sides of axial zone.

Transverse thin sections of holotype and a paratype taken at several positions along corallum. Data for these tabulated as follows (estimated measurements indicated):

Type	Average diameter of corallum (mm)	Number of primary septa	Width of axial complex (mm)	Width of dissepimentarium (mm)	Approximate height of section above apex (mm)
Holotype No.					
10862a	8	30	2	0.5	10
10862b	13	43	2–3	0.5–1	18
10862c	16	45	4	2	30
10862d	20	48	7	2	36
Paratype No.					
10863	30	75	10	4	45

DISCUSSION: The species is named in honor of Prof. Erwin C. Stumm of the University of Michigan.

Phaulactis stummi differs from previously described species in having a fairly well-defined axial complex.

Family STAURIIDAE Milne-Edwards and Haime

Genus *Favistella* Dana, 1846

Type Species: *Columnaria alveolata* Goldfuss, 1826

Bassler (1950, p. 271) recently discussed this genus, as follows:

"As now restricted, *Favistella* comprises compound tetracorals composed of polygonal, usually contiguous corallites united by their walls, without mural pores but with septa well developed as thin lamellae arranged in primary and secondary rows extending nearly to center of calyx, with complete horizontal tabulae and finally with no columella, dissepiments, or interstitial tissue."

Favistella alveolata (Goldfuss)

1826 *Columnaria alveolata* GOLDFUSS, Petrefacta Germaniae, v. 1, p. 72, Pl. 24, figs. 7a–c
1950 *Favistella alveolata* (Goldfuss). BASSLER, Geol. Soc. America Mem. 44, p. 271, Pl. 16, fig. 3 (includes detailed synonymy)

OCCURRENCE: Rare in Member No. 1 of Portage Chute Formation, North Knife River: locality 25314; and in Member No. 2, Churchill River: locality 25272. Rare in Member No. 1 of Chasm Creek Formation, Churchill River: locality 25283

Favistella alveolata var. *stellaris* (Wilson)

(Pl. 5, fig. 2)

1926 *Columnaria alveolata* n. var. *stellaris* WILSON, Geol. Surv. Canada Bull. 44, Geol. Ser. 46, p. 16, Pl. 3, figs. 1, 2
1950 *Favistella alveolata stellaris* (Wilson). BASSLER, Geol. Soc. America Mem. 44, p. 273

OCCURRENCE: One specimen (hypotype, G.S.C. No. 10843) from Chasm Creek Formation, Nelson River: locality 25267

DESCRIPTION: Wilson erected variety for specimens having small corallites, generally 2–3 mm, wide and with relatively fewer septa and more closely spaced tabulae than typical *F. alveolata*. Between 10–12 primary septa extend to center and alternate with very short secondary ones. Walls of individual corallites, although closely appressed, not amalgamated.

Chasm Creek specimen appears most closely related to this variety. Individual corallites polygonal, generally six-sided, and tend to be nearly equal in size with diameter between 2 and 2.5 mm.

In thin section contact between adjacent walls stands out clearly. Number of primary septa generally 10 or 11, and they extend directly to center with very little twisting. Secondary septa of most specimens about ⅛ mm in length.

Tabulae flat, and spaced, as in Wilson's specimens, about 1 mm apart.

DISCUSSION: The type specimen is from the Beaverfoot Formation in the Kananaskis area of the Rocky Mountains, British Columbia.

Order TABULATA Milne-Edwards and Haime
Family SYRINGOPHYLLIDAE Pocta
Genus *Nyctopora* Nicholson, 1879
Type Species: *Nyctopora billingsi* Nicholson, 1879

This genus includes species with thin-walled polygonal corallites. Walls appear to be amalgamated. In neanic stages septa are absent, but in maturity they are present as short vertical ridges or lamellae which may extend to the center of the corallite only on the floor of a tabula. In most specimens 8 primary septa and additional alternating secondary septa are present.

Tabulae are flat and relatively closely spaced.

Nyctopora(?) *foerstei* Bassler(?)

1950 *Nyctopora*(?) *foerstei* BASSLER, Geol. Soc. America Mem. 44, p. 264, Pl. 14, figs. 8, 9

OCCURRENCE: Common in Member No. 1 of Portage Chute Formation, North Knife River: localities 25313, 25314

DISCUSSION: To this species Bassler (1950) assigned coralla consisting of regularly pentagonal, thick-walled corallites averaging 1.6 mm in diameter and possessing septa varying in tangential sections from short, irregular spines to thick, rounded-triangular structures which project about a third the distance to the center of the corallite.

The tabulae are thin and closely spaced. In mature stages about six occur in a corallite diameter.

Bassler (1950, p. 264) was uncertain as to whether or not this species belonged to *Nyctopora* and stated:

"Many corallite junction angles occupied by thick, untabulated tube of dense tissue piled in cone-upon-cone arrangement. In transverse sections these show as oval bodies of concentric layers, but, in spite of numerous thin sections of the type and also the Lake St. John specimen, their nature has not been ascertained. Thin sections also fail to show whether septa are in series of 12 or, as usual in *Nyctopora*, in 8."

The present writer has little to add to Bassler's observations. Although many of the wall angles of the North Knife River specimens do show thickening no cone-in-cone structure was observed, either in transverse or longitudinal sections. Furthermore, septa are too obscure to be counted so that the specimens are questionably referred to this species.

The holotype is from the Waynesville Shale (Richmondian) of Ohio. The species also occurs in the Richmondian of Lake St. John.

Nyctopora mackenziei sp. nov.
(Pl. 6, figs. 3, 5)

OCCURRENCE: Fairly common in Member No. 1 of Portage Chute Formation, North Knife River: locality 25313; and in Member No. 2, Churchill River: locality 25272. Also fairly common in the Lower Member of Surprise Creek Formation Nelson River: localities 25259, 25262, 25264

Holotype, G.S.C. No. 10376: Lower Member, Surprise Creek Formation, Nelson River, locality 25262
Paratype, G.S.C. No. 10377: Member No. 1, Portage Chute Formation, North Knife River, locality 25313

DESCRIPTION: Corallum of thin-walled polygonal corallites having mature diameter of 3–3.5 mm. Line of contact between adjoining walls of corallites seen only in few places. Walls of most specimens amalgamated and total thickness 0.15–0.20 mm. Approximately 10 septa present in each corallite only near upper surface of each tabula where they extend halfway to center.

Tabulae 1.5–2 mm apart in mature corallites, nearly horizontal but some deflected gently down-ward at margins.

DISCUSSION: This species differs from typical members of *Nyctopora* in that ten septa are present instead of eight. *Nyctopora mackenziei* can also be distinguished by the large diameter of its corallites: most species have an average diameter of 1.5 mm or less (Bassler, 1950, p. 261–264).

The species is named in honor of the late Professor G. S. MacKenzie of the University of New Brunswick.

Genus *Saffordophyllum* Bassler, 1950
Type Species: *Saffordophyllum deckeri* Bassler, 1950

The genus *Saffordophyllum* was erected by Bassler (1950, p. 267) for coralla containing closely appressed polygonal tabulate corallites that are essentially a primitive *Nyctopora*. It is characterized by having undulating walls from which short wedgelike septa arise from the convex inward sides. It differs from *Nyctopora* in that the septa emerge from undulating, not straight, walls. Bassler made no mention of mural pores occurring in this genus, but the illustrations of two of the five species which he assigned to it suggest that they may be present. These two are *S. undulatum* Bassler (Bassler, Pl. 13, figs. 1, 2) and *S. kiaeri* Bassler (Pl. 18, fig. 4). The possible pores appear as breaks in the wall angles. In the new species *S.* (?) *portagechutense*, pores at angles are also present. It would seem, therefore, that Bassler's definition of the genus should be revised to include mural pores or else the genus should be split so as to include species with mural pores (*S. undulatum*, *S. kiaeri*, *S. portagechutense*) and those without (*S. deckeri*, *S. tabulatum*, *S. franklini*). The writer suggests that before such splitting be done, more work is needed to show whether or not mural pores are present in the last three species. Their apparent absence may be due to preservation or to chance placing of transverse sections.

Saffordophyllum(?) *portagechutense* sp. nov.
(Pl. 6, fig. 1)

OCCURRENCE: Common in Member No. 2 of Portage Chute Formation, Nelson River: locality 25257; Churchill River: localities 25271, 25274; and South Knife River: locality 25297

Holotype, G.S.C. No. 10327: Member No. 2, Portage Chute Formation, South Knife River, locality 25297

DESCRIPTION: Corallum, known only from fragments, apparently depressed hemispherical, consists of large, relatively thin-walled corallites about 3.5 mm in diameter, in which approximately 20 upward-pointing thornlike septa arise from convex-inward crenulations of walls. In transverse sections mural pores abundantly developed in wall angles and occur as breaks 0.25 mm–0.30 mm wide.

Tabulae very well developed, closely spaced and average 10–12 in 5 mm. They vary from horizontal to slightly convex upward.

DISCUSSION: Longitudinal sections show the septa of this species to be numerous, and in most corallites they arise in the interspaces between tabulae. In some specimens, however, they may appear only at intervals; one for every two or three interspaces. The vertical angle between the wall and the axis of the thornlike septa ranges from 45° to 80°.

Saffordophyllum(?) *portagechutense* is most closely related to *S. franklini* (Salter) but differs in that the average diameter of the corallites is about 0.5 mm larger, and septa average 20 instead of 12 in number. Another apparent difference is that the former species has mural pores, whereas the thin sections of *S. franklini*, illustrated by Bassler, do not show them.

The writer was impressed with the similarity between *Saffordophyllum*(?) *portagechutense* and *Calapoecia coxi* Bassler. Both have approximately the same corallite diameters and the same number of septa—20—the number which characterizes the genus *Calapoecia*. *Saffordophyllum*(?) *portage-chutense*, however, seems referable to the genus *Saffordophyllum* in its undulating walls and alternating septa. Although Bassler (1950, p. 267) stated that 8 primary septa were characteristic of

Saffordophyllum, his list of the species of this genus showed the number to reach a maximum of 20. It is possible then, that *Calapoecia coxi* may actually belong in this genus in which case the trivial name *coxi* has priority over *portagechutense*. Before joining the two, however, the writer suggests that the types of both be compared directly because the illustrations of *C. coxi* do not clearly show undulating walls or alternating septa.

Genus *Lyopora* Nicholson and Etheridge, 1878
Type Species: *Palaeopora? favosa* McCoy, 1850

Nicholson and Etheridge's (1878, p. 25) original diagnosis of this genus is as follows:

"Corallum composite, massive, composed of tubular, sub-cylindrical or hexagonal corallites, which are more or less completely fused with one another. Walls of the corallites extraordinarily thick and dense, destitute of mural pores. Columella absent. Septa rudimentary, few in number, having the form of irregular obtuse ridges on the interior of the wall. Tabulae complete. No coenenchyma."

The two new species which the present writer is referring to this genus differ from most of the previously described forms in that the corallite walls are much thinner. In nearly all other essentials, however, they agree closely with this genus.

Lyopora manitobensis sp. nov.
(Pl. 5, figs. 3a, b, 5a, b)

OCCURRENCE: Caution Creek Formation: fairly common in Member No. 1, Churchill River: localities 25281, 25282; and in Upper Member, South Knife River: localities 25302, 25305. Fairly common in Chasm Creek Formation on Nelson River: locality 25267; and in Member No. 1, Churchill River: localities 25281, 25282, 25283; and Member No. 3: locality 25290

Holotype, G.S.C. No. 10339: Member No. 1 Chasm Creek Formation, Churchill River, locality 25283
Paratype, G.S.C. No. 10340: Member No. 3, Chasm Creek Formation, Churchill River, locality 25290

DESCRIPTION: Corallum depressed hemispherical and at least 80 mm high. Corallites polygonal, almost all 5–6-sided, generally same size and average about 1.5 mm in diameter. Corallite walls appear amalgamated and about 0.2 mm thick. In transverse sections small obscure obtuse septa arise from walls at intervals and give walls irregularly swollen almost vesicular appearance.

Tabulae flat, closely spaced, about two in corallite diameter in immature stages and four in mature stages.

DISCUSSION: This species differs from *L. favosa* (McCoy), *L. americana* Bassler, and *L. ottawaensis* Bassler in having much smaller corallites. It appears to be most closely related to *L. nicholsoni* Raduguin from the Upper Ordovician of the Gornaya Shoria district of western Siberia. Raduguin's (1936, Pl. 1, figs. 3, 4, 6; Pl. 2, figs. 7, 10) illustrations, however, are poor. The main difference that can be seen from his figures is that in *L. nicholsoni* the tabulae are much more widely spaced than in *L. manitobensis*.

Lyopora manitobensis is also present in the Stony Mountain Shale Member of the Stony Mountain Formation. In the Department of Geology, University of Alberta, there is a specimen from this unit clearly referable to this species.

Lyopora churchillensis sp. nov.
(Pl. 6, figs. 2, 4a, b)

OCCURRENCE: Chasm Creek Formation: common on Nelson River: localities 25267, 25269; and in Member No. 1, Churchill River: localities 25282, 25283; and Member No. 2: localities 25285, 25286

Holotype, G.S.C. No. 10335: Member No. 1, Chasm Creek Formation, Churchill River, locality 25283
Paratype, G.S.C. No. 10336: Member No. 2, Chasm Creek Formation, Churchill River, locality 25285

DESCRIPTION: Shape of corallum unknown. Corallites polygonal, most 5–6-sided, generally equally sized, and average from 2 to 2.5 mm in diameter. Walls appear amalgamated and about 0.15 mm thick. Very small, thornlike septa arise at irregular intervals and give walls rather prickly appearance.

Tabulae flat and closely spaced: about three in corallite diameter in immature stages and about four in mature stages.

DISCUSSION: With some justification L. churchillensis could be considered a variety of L. manitobensis. The characteristic corallite diameters of both these species, however, remain remarkably constant, and no specimens have been found with intergradational corallites in mature stages. The walls of L. manitobensis in thin sections have a rather swollen appearance owing to the obscure obtuse septa, whereas those of L. churchillensis are prickly in aspect because of the thin acute septa.

Lyopora churchillensis is closely allied to L. ottawaensis Bassler. The walls of the latter, however, are much thinner.

Genus *Calapoecia* Billings, 1865

Type Species: *Calapoecia anticostiensis* Billings, 1865

The most comprehensive study that has been made of this puzzling genus was by Cox (1936). His diagnosis (p. 2) was as follows:

"Corallum massive hemispherical, irregularly spherical or encrusting. Corallites polygonal or circular; walls composed of fused septal elements, with pores on vertical and horizontal rows, alternating with the septa. Septa typically twenty, wedge-shaped, radiating, of equal length, short, usually extending one-fifth or less of the diameter into the corallite, inclined slightly upward. Tabulae well developed, complete and incomplete. No dissepiments. A coenenchyme may or may not be present; if it is, twenty 'costae' radiate from the corallites. Buds arise from between corallites."

Cox reduced the seven previously described species of *Calapoecia* to one: *C. canadensis* Billings; and under this species recognized the following varieties (Cox, p. 6–7):

C. canadensis Billings	Corallites in contact: no coenenchyme
C. canadensis var. *ungava* Cox	Corallites in contact and distant: little or no coenenchyme. Considered intermediate between *C. canadensis* and *C. anticostiensis*
C. canadensis var. *anticostiensis* (Billings)	Corallites circular and distant: costae and coenenchyme present
C. canadensis var. *anticostiensis* forma *arctica* (Troedsson)	Corallites 3–6 mm in diameter. Considered giant form of *anticostiensis*

Bassler (1950, p. 275–276) has recently restudied the genus and elevated the variety *anticostiensis* and the form *arctica* back to full species rank. In addition he resurrected *C. huronensis*, which Cox had placed in synonymy under *C. canadensis*, and described a new species *C. coxi*.

Using Bassler's classification the genus can be divided as follows:

(1) *Species with corallites in contact: no coenenchyme*

C. canadensis Billings	Polygonal corallites approximately 3 mm wide
C. huronensis Billings	Similar to *C. canadensis* but has more delicate septa. Disruptive canals usually present
C. coxi Bassler	Similar to *C. canadensis* but has more regularly polygonal corallites and stronger, thicker wedge-shaped septa arranged back to back in most specimens

(2) *Species with corallites separated by spaces occupied by coenenchyme*

C. canadensis var. *ungava* Cox	Small corallites; coenenchyme narrow
C. anticostiensis Billings	Corallites circular; separated by coenenchyme made up of costae and tabulae
C. arctica Troedsson	Giant *C. anticostiensis* with corallites more than 3 mm in diameter and intervening spaces similarly large

Calapoecia anticostiensis Billings
(Pl. 8, fig. 5, Pl. 10, fig. 4)

1865 *Calapoecia anticostiensis* BILLINGS, Canadian Nat. and Geol., New Ser., v. 2, p. 426
1936 *Calapoecia canadensis* var. *anticostiensis* (Billings). Cox, Nat. Mus. Canada Bull. 80, Geol. Ser. 53, p. 12, Pl. 1, fig. 6; Pl. 3, figs. 1a–c, 3d, 5a–c, 6, 7 (includes synonymy list)

1941 *Calapoecia canadensis* var. *anticostiensis* (Billings). ROY, Field Mus. Nat. Hist., Geol. Mem., v. 2, p. 74, figs. 38a–d
1950 *Calapoecia anticostiensis* Billings. BASSLER, Geol. Soc. America Mem. 44, p. 276, Pl. 20, figs. 9, 10

OCCURRENCE: Rare in Member No. 2 of Portage Chute Formation, Churchill River: locality 25274. Rare in Lower Member of Surprise Creek Formation, Nelson River: locality 25260. Fairly common in Member No. 1 of Caution Creek Formation, Churchill River: localities 25277, 25281; and in Upper Member of this formation, South Knife River: locality 25302. Common in Member No. 1 of Chasm Creek Formation, Churchill River: localities 25282, 25283; and in Member No. 2: locality 25285

Hypotype, G.S.C. No. 10502: Member No. 1, Chasm Creek Formation, Churchill River, locality 25283
Hypotype, G.S.C. No. 10380: Member No. 2, Chasm Creek Formation, Churchill River, locality 25285

DISCUSSION: Two distinct kinds of coralla are recognized in the northern Manitoban material referred to this species. The first (hypotype 10380) which are typical *C. anticostiensis*, have corallites with a diameter varying between 2 and 3 mm. Specimens of the second kind (hypotype 10502) have much smaller corallites, averaging about 1.5 mm in diameter, which are surrounded by relatively wide zones of coenenchymal material. One specimen of the second kind has been found in the Upper Member of the Caution Creek Formation (locality 25302) on the South Knife, but most occur in the upper part of Member No. 1 of the Chasm Creek at locality 25823, Churchill River. They appear to be characteristic of this last horizon.

Examination of Anticosti Island specimens of *C. anticostiensis* in the National Museum of Canada showed that the above two kinds are present. Until more specimens are available for study it cannot be said whether these differences in corallite diameter are specific, varietal, or individual.

Calapoecia anticostiensis has a wide geographic range in the Upper Ordovician (Cox, 1936, p. 12–16). Okulitch (1943, p. 63) listed it from the Gunton Member of the Stony Mountain Formation of southern Manitoba. On Anticosti Island it ranges throughout the Upper Ordovician sequence.

Calapoecia arctica Troedsson(?)

1928 *Calapoecia arctica* TROEDSSON, Medd. om Grønland, v. 72, p. 127, Pl. 39; Pl. 40, figs. 1a, b
1936 *Calapoecia canadensis* var. *anticostiensis* forma *arctica* (Troedsson). Cox, Nat. Mus. Canada Bull. 80, Geol. Ser. 53, p. 16, Pl. 4, figs. 1a, b, 2a, b, 3
1950 *Calapoecia arctica* Troedsson. BASSLER, Geol. Soc. America Mem. 44, p. 276, Pl. 20, figs. 7, 8

OCCURRENCE: Common in Member No. 1 of Portage Chute Formation, North Knife River: localities 25313, 25314. Rare in Member No. 2 of this formation, South Knife River: locality 25294

DISCUSSION: Troedsson placed in this species Calapoecias in which the diameters of the individual corallites ranged between 4 and 6 mm but Cox (1936) stated that the diameter may be as little as 3 mm. Because of the wide corallite spacing Cox (p. 17) concluded that *C. arctica* "... can be regarded as no more than a form of var. *anticostiensis* from which they differ only in size. It is convenient rather than essential that they should have a name, because their form seems to be restricted to the north Arctic region and is easily recognized externally. Following the conventions their relation to the other forms of *Calapoecia* can only be expressed as *C. canadensis* var. *anticostiensis* forma *arctica*. This may be cumbersome, but, as shown above, they are only a local race of the variety *anticostiensis* ..."

Bassler (1950, p. 276) in his study of *Calapoecia* recognized Troedsson's species and stated that it "... is indeed a giant *C. anticostiensis*... with corallite diameters over 3 mm and intervening spaces similarly large..."

The writer is questionably referring to this species specimens in which the corallite diameters range from 3 to 3.5 mm. In some of these specimens the intervening spaces are large, but in others they are so narrow as to almost resemble *C. canadensis* which, however, has much smaller corallites. The reference to *C. arctica* is questioned, because in the present specimens the corallites are smaller, and the interspaces more variable in size.

Calapoecia canadensis var. *ungava* Cox
(Pl. 10, fig. 3)

1936 *Calapoecia canadensis* var. *ungava* Cox, Nat. Mus. Canada Bull. 80, Geol. Ser. 53, p. 12, Pl. 3, fig. 2, (includes detailed synonymy)
1950 *Calapoecia canadensis ungava* Cox. BASSLER, Geol. Soc. America Mem. 44, p. 276

OCCURRENCE: Rare in Member No. 1 of Caution Creek Formation, Churchill River: locality 25281; and in Upper Member of this formation, South Knife River: localities 25303, 25304. Rare in Member No. 1 of Chasm Creek Formation, Churchill River: locality 25282; and in Member No. 3: locality 25290

Hypotype, G.S.C. No. 10503: Upper Member, Caution Creek Formation, South Knife River, locality 25304

DISCUSSION: The writer has placed in this species specimens in which corallite diameters average about 2 mm or slightly less, and the spaces between are very narrow but well enough developed so that costae can be easily seen.

Calapoecia canadensis var. *ungava* occurs in the Upper Ordovician of Akpatok Island. Bassler (1950, p. 22) listed the species from the Stony Mountain Formation of southern Manitoba but not in the underlying Red River Formation. Baillie (1952, p. 28; *see* also p. 32), on the other hand, indicated it only from the Red River. Cox (1936, p. 12) considered that the specimens described by Lambe (1899, p. 45) from the Selkirk Member (= Dog Head) of the Red River belonged to this variety

Family HELIOLITIDAE Lindström
Genus *Protrochiscolithus* Troedsson, 1928
Type Species: *Protrochiscolithus kiaeri* Troedsson, 1928
Protrochiscolithus kiaeri Troedsson
(Pl. 7, figs. 7, 8)

1928 *Protrochiscolithus kiaeri* TROEDSSON, Medd. om Grønland, v. 72, p. 116, fig. 2; Pl. 30, figs. 1a–c; Pl. 46, fig. 2
1952 *Protrochiscolithus kiaeri* Troedsson. LEITH, Jour. Pal., v. 26, no. 5, p. 792, Pl. 114, figs. 1–9; Pl. 115, figs. 1–6

OCCURRENCE: Rare in Member No. 1 of Caution Creek Formation, Churchill River: locality 25281; and in Upper Member, South Knife River: locality 25305. Rare in Chasm Creek Formation, Nelson River: locality 25296; but fairly common in Member No. 2 of this formation, Churchill River: localities 25283, 25284, 25288

Hypotypes, G.S.C. No. 10853, 10859: Member No. 2, Chasm Creek Formation, Churchill River: localities 25288, 25283, respectively

DISCUSSION: Specimens referred to this species are almost identical with those illustrated by Troedsson and Leith. Leith has given a very complete description of the species and its probable systematic position.

Protrochiscolithus kiaeri is most common in Member No. 2 of the Chasm Creek Formation. In southern Manitoba it occurs in the Selkirk Member (= Dog Head) of the Red River Formation. The types are from the Cape Calhoun Series of northern Greenland.

Genus *Plasmopora* Milne-Edwards and Haime, 1849
Type Species: *Porites petaliformis* Lonsdale, 1839
Plasmopora lambei Schuchert

1900 *Plasmopora lambii* SCHUCHERT, United States Nat. Mus. Proc., v. 22, p. 154
1915 *Plasmopora lambii* Schuchert. BASSLER, United States Nat. Mus. Bull. 92, v. 2, p. 983
1925 *Plasmopora lambii* Schuchert. HUME, Geol. Surv. Canada Mem. 145, Pl. 5, figs. 1a, b
1928 *Plasmopora lambi* Schuchert [*partim*]. TROEDSSON, Medd. om Grønland, v. 72, p. 118, Pl. 32, fig. 1
1937 [*non*] *Plasmopora lambei* Schuchert. TEICHERT, Rept. Fifth Thule Exp., 1921–1924, v. 1, no. 5, p. 53, Pl. 4, fig. 13; Pl. 5, figs. 1, 2

1941 *Plasmopora lambei* Schuchert. Roy, Field Mus. Nat. Hist. Geol. Mem., v. 2, p. 70, figs. 36a–f
1954 *Plasmopora lambii* Schuchert. MILLER, YOUNGQUIST, and COLLINSON, Geol. Soc. America Mem. 62, p. 11, Pl. 8, figs. 4–7

OCCURRENCE: Common in Member No. 1 of Portage Chute Formation, North Knife River: localities 25312, 25313, 25314; and in Member No. 2 of this formation, Nelson, Churchill, and South Knife rivers: nearly all areas of outcrop. Rare in Member No. 1 of Surprise Creek Formation, Churchill River: locality 25272; and in Lower Member of this formation, Nelson River: locality 25259

Hypotypes, G.S.C. No. 10378, 10379: Member No. 2, Portage Chute Formation, Churchill River, localities 25275, 25271, respectively

DISCUSSION: *Plasmopora lambei* appears to be an abundant and characteristic member of the Red River Arctic fauna. Besides thn northern Manitoban occurrences it is known from the Frobisher Bay outlier at Baffin Island (Schuchert, 1900; Roy, 1941; Miller, Youngquist, and Collinson, 1954), the Cape Calhoun Series of northern Greenland (Troedsson, 1928), Iglulik Island and Melville Peninsula (Teichert, 1937), and the Liskeard Formation of the Lake Timiskaming area (Hume, 1925).

Plasmopora pattersoni Roy

1928 *Plasmopora lambi* Schuchert [*partim*]. TROEDSSON, Medd. om Grønland, v. 72, p. 118, Pl. 31, figs. 1a, b; Pl. 32, fig. 2; Pl. 33, figs. 1a, b
1937 *Plasmopora lambei* Schuchert. TEICHERT, Rept. Fifth Thule Exp., 1921–1924, v. 1, no. 5, p. 53, Pl. 4, fig. 13; Pl. 5, figs. 1, 2
1941 *Plasmopora pattersoni* ROY, Field Mus. Nat. Hist. Geol. Mem., v. 2, p. 72, figs. 37a–e

OCCURRENCE: Rare in Member No. 2 of Portage Chute Formation, Churchill River: locality 25270; and Nelson River: localities 25257, 25258

DISCUSSION: The primary types of *P. pattersoni* are from the Frobisher Bay outlier of Baffin Island (Roy, 1941). Besides northern Manitoba it is also known from the Cape Calhoun Series of northern Greenland (Troedsson, 1928) and from Iglulik Island and Melville Peninsula (Teichert, 1937).

Family FAVOSITIDAE Dana
Genus *Palaeofavosites* Twenhofel, 1914
Type Species: *Favosites asper* D'Orbigny, 1850

Stearn (1956) has recently given an excellent discussion of this genus and interpreted it to include tabulate corals with nearly all characteristics of *Favosites*, except that most mural pores occur in wall angles and few in the walls.

Extensive collections of this genus have been made in northern Manitoba, and three well-defined species can be recognized. Unfortunately the various species of *Palaeofavosites* have been given such a variety of interpretation in the past that the writer is not certain where to refer his material. An additional complication is that most primary type material has never been adequately described and/or illustrated. Where possible the writer has followed or interpreted the original description of a species and referred his specimens to that species only if he considers that their characteristics warrant it. It must be realized that later revision of the genus may show that the Manitoba specimens belong in quite different species. It is hoped that the descriptions and i lustrations, presented below, will be adequate to enable future workers to determine their true systematic position in event of such revision.

Palaeofavosites alveolaris (Lonsdale)(?)
(Pl. 7, fig. 9)

1839 *Favosites alveolaris* LONSDALE, Murchison's Sil. Syst., p. 681, Pl. 15, figs. 1, 2

OCCURRENCE: Common in Upper Member of Caution Creek Formation, South Knife River: localities 25304, 25305; and in Member No. 3, Churchill River: locality 25281. Two specimens from

Chasm Creek Formation, Nelson River: locality 25269; three from Member No. 1 of this formation, Churchill River: locality 25281; and one from Member No. 2: locality 25283

Hypotype, G.S.C. No. 10331: Chasm Creek Formation, Nelson River, locality 25269

DESCRIPTION: Coralla referred to this species have rather regularly shaped and sized, thin-walled, for most part 6-sided polygonal corallites, 2.5–3.0 mm in diameter. No specimens have mural pores preserved on weathered surfaces, but in thin sections they are common in wall angles and have diameters of about 0.2 mm.

Tabulae flat. In most specimens three occur in distance equal to corallite diameter in immature stages and six in mature stages.

DISCUSSION: The Hudson Bay Lowland specimens appear most similar to the European *P. alveolaris* (Lonsdale) and *P. asper* (D'Orbigny). Milne-Edwards and Haime (1854, p. 258) distinguished *P. asper* from the former by its greater irregularity of corallite dimensions. As the present specimens are characterized by a rather regular corallite size and shape, they are referred to *P. alveolaris*.

Palaeofavosites prolificus (Billings)
(Pl. 7, fig. 5)

1865 *Favosites prolificus* BILLINGS, Canadian Nat. and Geol., v. 2, p. 429
1866 *Favosites prolificus* Billings. BILLINGS, Cat. Sil. Foss. Anticosti, p. 6, 32
1895 *Favosites prolificus* Billings. WHITEAVES, Geol. Surv. Canada Pal. Foss., v. 3, pt. 2, p. 113
1899 *Favosites aspera* D'Orbigny [*partim*]. LAMBE, Geol. Surv. Canada Contr. Canadian Pal., v. 4 pt. 1, p. 4, Pl. 1, fig. 2
1910 *Favosites? prolificus* Billings. SCHUCHERT and TWENHOFEL, Geol. Soc. America Bull., v. 21, p. 696
1914 *Paleofavosites prolificus* (Billings). TWENHOFEL, Nat. Mus. Canada Bull. 3, Geol. Ser. 19, p. 24
1928 *Paleofavosites prolificus* (Billings). TWENHOFEL, Geol. Surv. Canada Mem. 154, p. 126
1944 *Paleofavosites prolificus* (Billings). SHIMER and SHROCK, Index Fossils of North America, p. 107, Pl. 37, fig. 17
1956 *Paleofavosites prolificus* (Billings). STEARN, Geol. Surv. Canada Mem. 281, p. 60, Pl. 4, fig. 1; Pl. 10, fig. 13

OCCURRENCE: Two specimens from Chasm Creek Formation, Churchill River. One (hypotype, G.S.C. No. 10329) is from Member No. 1: locality 25281; and the other from Member No. 2: locality 25285

DESCRIPTION: Coralla referred to this species have thin-walled, rather regularly sized and shaped polygonal corallites most of which are 6-sided and about 1.5 mm in diameter. Mural pores common in wall angles and have diameter of about 0.1 mm.

Tabulae flat and closely spaced. Between four and six occur in distance equal to corallite diameter.

DISCUSSION: In southern Manitoba Okulitch (1943) has identified this Anticosti Island species from the Penitentiary and Gunton members of the Stony Mountain Formation. Baillie (1952) and Stearn (1956) have also reported it from the overlying Stonewall Formation and Interlake Group.

Palaeofavosites capax Billings
(Pl. 7, fig. 4)

1866 *Favosites? capax* BILLINGS, Cat. Sil. Foss. Anticosti, p. 6
1899 *Favosites aspera* D'Orbigny [*partim*]. LAMBE, Geol. Surv. Canada, Contr. Canadian Pal., v. 4, p. 4
1943 *Paleofavosites capax* (Billings). OKULITCH, Trans. Roy. Soc. Canada, v. 37, sec. 4, Pl. 1, fig. 17
1956 *Paleofavosites capax* (Billings). STEARN, Geol. Surv. Canada Mem. 281, p. 61, Pl. 10, fig. 12

OCCURRENCE· Two specimens from Member No. 1 of Caution Creek Formation, Churchill River: localities 25281, 25282; and one from Upper Member, South Knife River: locality 25302. Two specimens from Chasm Creek Formation, Nelson River: localities 25267, 25269; and four from Member No. 1 of this formation, Churchill River: localities 25281, 25283

Hypotype, G.S.C. No. 10355: Member No. 1, Caution Creek Formation, Churchill River, locality 25282

DESCRIPTION: Writer refers coralla to this Anticosti Island species in which most mature corallites attain diameters of 4–5 mm. Corallites typically unequally sized and shaped. Immature forms interspaced between mature ones, have 3–5 sides, and diameter varying between 2 and 3 mm. Most mature corallites irregularly polygonal and have 6–7 sides. Mural pores common in wall angles and have diameter varying between 0.2 and 0.3 mm.

Tabulae numerous and flat. In most immature corallites 3–4 occur in distance equal to corallite diameter, and in mature forms 7–8 occur in a diameter.

DISCUSSION: Billings' (1866, p. 6) original description of *P. capax* stated that mature corallites have a diameter of two lines (approximately 4 mm) and that immature forms were scattered among them. The specimens which the present writer is referring to this species agree well, in these features, with Billings' (*loc. cit.*) diagnosis but not with Twenhofel's (1928, p. 126) description. The latter author stated that the corallites in his specimens had diameters between 2 and 3 mm. Until the confusion regarding *P. capax* is cleared up the writer thinks it best to follow Billings' diagnosis.

Palaeofavosites capax has been identified from numerous localities in North America. Unfortunately, most identifications are without descriptions or illustrations so that affinities with the northern Manitoban material cannot be determined. Okulitch (1943) has identified *P. capax* from the Stony Mountain Shale and Gunton (Birse interval) members of the Stony Mountain Formation, southern Manitoba. He illustrated an immature corallum in which the diameters of the largest corallites are about 2 mm. The writer has examined his specimen and found it similar to an immature *P. capax* from Member No. 1 of the Chasm Creek Formation so that the present writer is including Okulitch's identification in the synonymy. Baillie (1951) and Stearn (1956) have listed *P. capax* from the Stonewall Formation. The present writer has examined some of the material from this unit. It is almost identical with the specimens here referred to this species.

Palaeofavosites okulitchi Stearn
(Pl. 7, fig. 6)

1943 *Favosites intermedius* OKULITCH [non Stewart]. Trans. Roy. Soc. Canada, v. 37, sec. 4, p. 70, Pl. 1, fig. 16
1956 *Palaeofavosites okulitchi* STEARN. Geol. Surv. Canada Mem. 281, p. 61, Pl. 3, figs. 4, 6; Pl. 8, fig. 3
1959 *Palaeofavosites okulitchi* STEARN. HILL, New Mexico Inst. Min. Tech. Bull. 64, p. 11

OCCURRENCE: Five specimens from upper beds of Member No. 1 of Chasm Creek Formation, Churchill River: locality 25283; one from Member No. 2: locality 25284; and two from Member No. 3: locality 25290

Hypotype, G.S.C. No. 10351: Member No. 2, Chasm Creek Formation, Churchill River, locality 25283

DESCRIPTION: Coralla from Churchill River have more or less regularly polygonal, 5- to 6-sided mature corallites with diameters ranging from 2 to 3 mm, although some attain dimensions of 3.5 mm. Numerous immature, generally four-sided corallites interspersed between them. No specimens showing mural pores on weathered surfaces have been found. Thin sections, however, show mural pores in both wall angles and walls. Most pores range in diameter from 0.2 to 0.3 mm.

Tabulae flat and relatively closely spaced, about three occur in distance equal to corallite diameter in immature stages, and five–seven in mature stages.

DISCUSSION: The holotype of *P. okulitchi*, from the Gunton Member of the Stony Mountain Formation, southern Manitoba, has corallites 2–3 mm in diameter. They are usually three- to seven-sided, and six-sided forms are most common. Mural pores are in both wall angles and walls. The species has also been found in the Stonewall Formation (Baillie, 1951; Stearn, 1956).

Okulitch (1943) erected this species for corals which he considered intermediate between *Favosites* and *Palaeofavosites* in that pores occur in both angles and walls. Stearn (1956) in redefining the genus *Palaeofavosites* decided that the species should be placed here.

Genus *Favosites* Lamarck, 1812
Type Species: *Favosites gothlandicus* Lamarck, 1816

As revised by Stearn (1956) the genus *Favosites* is now considered to contain tabulate corals in which mural pores occur in the walls and none at all in the wall angles.

Favosites wilsonae sp. nov.
(Pl. 7, figs. 1, 2a, b, 3)

OCCURRENCE: Common in Member No. 1 of Caution Creek Formation, Churchill River: localities 25281, 25282; and in Member No. 3: locality 25281. Fairly common in Upper Member of this formation, South Knife River: localities 25304, 25306

Holotype, G.S.C. No. 10350: Upper Member, Caution Creek Formation, South Knife River. locality 25306
Paratype, G.S.C. No. 10348: Member No. 1, Caution Creek Formation, Churchill River, locality 25282
Paratype, G.S.C. No. 10349: Member No. 1, Caution Creek Formation, Churchill River, locality 25275

DESCRIPTION: Corallites thin-walled, polygonal, generally 5- to 6-sided and typically range in diameter from 1.3 to 1.7 mm. A few corallites reach diameter of 2.0 mm. Mural pores common and vary in diameter from 0.2 to 0.3 mm. They are surrounded by well-developed but very narrow and low rims. Arrangements of pores on corallite wall variable but most commonly two rows alternating or opposite in position.

Tabulae flat and closely spaced: about four occur in distance equal to corallite diameter.

DISCUSSION: *Favosites wilsonae* is named in honor of Dr. Alice Wilson of the Geological Survey of Canada.

The species appears to be most closely related to *F. forbesi* Milne-Edwards and Haime but differs in having corallites with fewer sides and a less variable diameter. Another rather similar species is *F. hisingeri* Milne-Edwards and Haime. *Favosites wilsonae* differs from it in that the corallite diameters tend to be, within the defined size limits, more irregular and slightly larger.

It has previously been stated in an abstract (Nelson, 1953, p. 1458) that *Favosites* was also found in the Red River equivalents of northern Manitoba. This *Favosites* is a single specimen of *F. wilsonae*, thought to be from Member No. 2 of the Portage Chute Formation on Churchill River at locality 25275. However, a later study of the collection revealed that a specimen of *Lobocorallium trilobatum* var. *major* definitely known to be from Member No. 1 of the Caution Creek Formation on Churchill River at locality 25278, was erroneously labelled with the same Portage Chute locality number as the specimen of *F. wilsonae*. Thus, there is a possibility that the latter may have been also erroneously labelled, and is actually from the Caution Creek Formation. Until future workers can determine whether the species occurs in the Portage Chute, it is thought best to delete it from the evidence regarding the age of the Bad Cache Rapids Group.

Family HALYSITIDAE Milne-Edwards and Haime
Genus *Catenipora* Lamarck, 1816
Type Species: *Catenipora escharoides* Lamarck, 1816

Buehler (1955) has recently discussed this genus in detail. It includes species formerly placed in the genus *Halysites* Fischer de Waldheim, but which have no mesocorallites (tubules). He gave an excellent discussion of the morphology of both *Halysites* and *Catenipora* and recommended adoption of a new terminology in describing these corals. The following are the most important terms used by Buehler:

Buehler's terminology	*Previously used terminology*
Autocorallites	Corallites, tubes
Mesocorallites	Tubules, tubuli
Tabulae	Tabulae
Ranks	Reticulations, rows
Lacunae	Fenestrules, meshes, intercellular spaces

Most representatives of the genus *Catenipora* are easily recognizable and, in North America, are confined mainly to the Red River and Stony Mountain Arctic faunal provinces (Nelson, 1959b).

In North America few Silurian and ?Devonian species are known. The great majority occur in the Upper Ordovician.

Sinclair (1955) has discussed the origin of forms placed in *Catenipora* and has suggested that three distinct genera are present. These are (1) *Catenipora* (*s. s.*) for corallites with septa; (2) *Quepora* for *Lichenaria*-like corals without septa, and (3) *Manipora* for *Saffordophyllum*-like corals with crenulated walls and a favositoid growth habit.

In the present writer's opinion *Quepora* should be considered a "form" genus. Numerous cateniporid specimens both from the Hudson Bay Lowland, and from oil company collections in Arctic areas suggest that development of septa is sporadic even within a single corallum. Moreover, wall structures of the type species of *Quepora*, and of specimens referred to *Catenipora* (*s. s.*) are similar in that both the theca and epitheca are present. Thus, *Quepora* is not at all like *Lichenaria*.

The favositoid specimens have two designs of wall structure. One, characteristic of true *Manipora*, has corallites with only one wall. Species which the present writer is referring to *Manipora* on this basis are *M. amicarum* Sinclair, *M. irregularis* (Teichert), and *M. feildeni* (Etheridge). The writer has not examined primary type material of the last two species. Hudson Bay Lowland specimens referred to them, however, have very poorly developed or no wall crenulations. The other, represented by *Catenipora stearni* sp. nov., has corallites with theca and epitheca and is considered to be a favositoid *C. robusta* (Wilson).

Catenipora rubra Sinclair and Bolton

(Pl. 14, figs. 1, 2)

1899 *Halysites catenularia* var. *gracilis* (Hall) [*partim*]. LAMBE, Geol. Surv. Canada Contr. Canadian
    Pal., v. 4, pt. 1, p. 69, Pl. 3, figs. 5, 5a, b, fig. 6 (?)
1928 *Halysites gracilis* (Hall). HUSSEY, Contr. Mus. Pal., Univ. Michigan, v. 3, no. 3, p. 71, Pl. 1,
    fig. 4
1931 [?] *Halysites gracilis* var. *borealis* WILSON, Trans. Roy. Soc. Canada, v. 25, sec. 4, p. 296, Pl. 3,
    fig. 5
1937 *Halysites gracilis* (Hall). TEICHERT, Rept. Fifth Thule Exped., 1921–1924, v. 1, no. 5, p. 55, Pl.
    7, figs. 3, 6
1941 *Halysites* cf. *H. gracilis* (Hall). ROY, Field Mus. Nat. Hist. Geol. Mem., v. 2, p. 79, figs. 40a, b
1944 *Halysites gracilis* (Hall) [*partim*]. LEITH, Jour. Pal., v. 18, no. 3, Pl. 43, figs. 5, 6
1944 *Halysites gracilis* (Hall). SHIMER and SHROCK, Index Fossils of North America, p. 113, Pl. 41,
    figs. 1–3
1955 *Catenipora gracilis* Hall. BUEHLER, Peabody Mus. Nat. Hist., Yale Univ. Bull. 8, p. 36, Pl. 4,
    fig. 7; Pl. 5, fig. 1
1955 [?] *Catenipora gracilis* var. *borealis* (Wilson). BUEHLER, Peabody Mus. Nat. Hist., Yale Univ.
    Bull. 8, p. 60
1955 *Catenipora rubra* Sinclair and Bolton. SINCLAIR, Trans. Roy. Soc. Canada, v. 59, sec. 4, p. 99,
    Pl. 1, figs. 2, 6, 7, 11; fig. 2
1956 *Catenipora rubra* SINCLAIR and BOLTON, Jour. Pal., v. 30, no. 1, p. 204

OCCURRENCE: Fairly common in Member No. 2 of Portage Chute Formation, Nelson River: localities 25254, 25257; and Churchill River: locality 25270. Rare in Member No. 1 of Caution Creek Formation, Churchill River: locality 25282. Rare in Chasm Creek Formation, Nelson River: locality 25267

Hypotype, G.S.C. No. 10896: Member No. 2, Portage Chute Formation, Nelson River, locality
25254
Hypotype, G.S.C. No. 10897: Chasm Creek Formation, Nelson River, locality 25267

DESCRIPTION: Specimens from northern Manitoba very similar to holotype. Corallites large, arranged in monoserial ranks, and within single corallum may have transverse exterior outline varying from subquadrate to subrectangular to subelliptical. Average length of mature corallite 2.2 mm and width at mid-length and appressed end 1.9 mm and 1.6 mm, respectively. Walls thin in comparison with size of corallites and not noticeably thickened at outer ends of appressed walls. Thus, transverse exterior outline rather similar to interior one. A few rare septal spines sporadically developed.

Tabulae flat and closely spaced: about four occur in distance equal to corallite mid-length width.

Lacunae large and vary in transverse outline from subelliptical to subquadrate to vermiform within corallum. A subelliptical or subquadrate lacuna may have maximum length of 20 mm and corresponding width of about 5 mm. Most vermiform lacunae less than 50 mm long.

DISCUSSION: *Catenipora rubra* is similar to *C. robusta*, and it is possible that they may be conspecific. The following differences, however, are noted.

(1) The corallites of *C. robusta* have a remarkably uniform subelliptical outline and most have a length and width of 1.7 mm and 1.2 mm respectively. Those of *C. rubra* appear to have a more variable transverse outline and are usually larger.

(2) The lacunae of *C. robusta* tend to be both elongated and narrow, whereas most of those of *C. rubra* are elongated but proportionally are relatively wider.

The writer is of the opinion that Wilson's (1931) *Halysites gracilis* var. *borealis* may be conspecific with *Catenipora rubra*, in which case *borealis* has priority over the trivial name *rubra*. More specimens of the variety are needed, however, before redesignation can be effected with certainty.

Catenipora robusta (Wilson)
(Pl. 14, figs. 3–5)

1899 [?] *Halysites catenularia* var. *gracilis* (Hall). LAMBE, Geol. Surv. Canada Contr. Canadian Pal.' v. 4, pt. 1, p. 74 (Specimen 4, Nelson River)
1926 *Halysites robustus* WILSON, Geol. Surv. Canada Bull. 44, Geol. Ser. 46, p. 14, Pl. 1, figs. 8–10
1928 *Halysites gracilis* (Hall). TROEDSSON, Medd. om Grønland, v. 72, p. 131, Pl. 40, figs. 2, 3
1955 *Catenipora robustus* (Wilson). BUEHLER, Peabody Mus. Nat. Hist., Yale Univ. Bull. 8, p. 58

OCCURRENCE: Fairly common in Member No. 2 of Portage Chute Formation on South Knife River: localities 25294, 25297; Churchill River: localities 25270, 25271; and Nelson River: locality 25257. Rare in Lower Member of Surprise Creek Formation, Nelson River: locality 25260. Rare in Member No. 1 of Caution Creek Formation, Churchill River: locality 25281; and in Upper Member, South Knife River: locality 25302. Fairly common in Member No. 1 of Chasm Creek Formation, Churchill River: locality 25281; and in this formation on Nelson River: localities 25267, 25269

Hypotype, G.S.C. No. 10890: Member No. 2, Portage Chute Formation, South Knife River, locality 25294
Hypotype, G.S.C. No. 10891: Member No. 2, Portage Chute Formation, Churchill River, locality 25270
Hypotype, G.S.C. No. 10368: Member No. 2, Portage Chute Formation, Nelson River, locality 25257

DESCRIPTION: Writer has examined holotype of *C. robusta* as well as possible topotype material from Beaverfoot Formation of British Columbia and found northern Manitoban specimens nearly identical with them. Individual corallites arranged in monoserial ranks and remarkably regular in both transverse shape and size. They are subelliptical in outline with narrow ends flattened and appressed against adjacent corallites. Length of nearly all mature corallites 1.7 mm; width at mid-length and appressed ends 1.2 mm and 1 mm, respectively; ratio of mid-length width to length 5:7. Immature corallites present in one specimen. Except for their smaller size, outline and proportions of width and length nearly identical with those of more mature individuals. Corallite walls in latter relatively thick, particularly so toward outer ends of appressed walls, and give interior elliptical outline, or, more rarely, subdued replica of exterior outline. Numerous spines present but poorly preserved.

Tabulae nearly flat, or some convex upward; between 0.5 to 1 mm apart: in most specimens two occur in distance equal to corallite mid-length width and show no noticeable change in spacing over corallite length.

Lacunae similar in transverse outline to those of *C. rubra* but smaller. Vary from subvermiform to subcircular and rarely twist at right angles. Maximum length of lacunae rarely more than 30 mm: in most specimens between 15 and 20 mm, and corresponding width about 5 mm.

Catenipora stearni sp. nov.
(Pl. 14, figs. 6, 7)

OCCURRENCE: Rare in Member No. 2 of Portage Chute Formation on Nelson River: locality 25257; and Churchill River: locality 25271. Rare in Member No. 1 of Caution Creek Formation, Churchill River: locality 25279

Holotype, G.S.C. No. 10895: Member No. 1, Caution Creek Formation, locality 25279
Paratype, G.S.C. No. 10369: Member No. 2, Portage Chute Formation, locality 25271

DESCRIPTION: Corallites arranged in monoserial and biserial but rarely in triserial ranks. Monoserial ranks common, and favositoid growth in most corallites occurs near junction of ranks. Monoserial corallites depressed circular in transverse exterior outline, and appressed walls relatively wide. Length and width average about 1.3 mm and 1.0 mm, respectively. Most favositoid corallites have polygonal or subpolygonal outline and average diameter of about 1.3 mm. Corallite walls relatively wide but not noticeably thickened at appressed ends so that interior outline similar to that of exterior.

Tabulae flat and relatively widely spaced, in most specimens three occur in distance equal to corallite mid-length width.

Lacunae similar in size and outline to those of *C. robusta* (Wilson).

DISCUSSION: The species is named in honor of Dr. Colin Stearn of McGill University.

This species is thought to have been derived from *C. robusta* to which it is closely related in size and outline of corallites and lacunae. In some specimens corallites in monoserial ranks are very similar in both size and transverse outline to those of *C. robusta*. In others, however, length was probably reduced owing to favositoid growth, and a similar width was retained at mid-length and appressed ends.

Specimens included in this species are very similar to those the writer refers to *Manipora irregularis* (Teichert). The wall structure of these two species, however, appears quite different.

Catenipora aequabilis (Teichert)
(Pl. 14, figs. 8, 9)

1926 [?] *Halysites gracilis* (Hall). HUSSEY, Contr. Mus. Geol., Univ. Michigan, v. 2, no. 8, Pl. 11, fig. 14
1931 *Halysites arcticus* WILSON [*nomen nudem*]. Trans. Roy. Soc. Canada, v. 25, sec. 4, p. 287
1931 *Halysites* cf. *feildeni* Etheridge. WILSON, Trans. Roy. Soc. Canada, v. 25, sec. 4, p. 297, Pl. 3, figs. 6, 7
1937 *Halysites aequabilis* TEICHERT. Rept. Fifth Thule Exped., 1921–1924, v. 1, no. 5, p. 57, Pl. 8, fig. 2; Pl. 9, fig. 4
1947a *Halysites* spp. MILLER and YOUNGQUIST [*partim*], Jour. Pal., v. 21, no. 1, p. 5, Pl. 7, fig. 9
1955 *Catenipora aequabilis* (Teichert). BUEHLER, Peabody Mus. Nat. Hist., Yale Univ. Bull. 8, p. 63

OCCURRENCE: Portage Chute Formation: common in Member No. 1, North Knife River: locality 25314. Rare in Member No. 2, South Knife River: locality 25299; Churchill River: locality 25275. Rare in Lower Member of Surprise Creek Formation, Nelson River: locality 25265

Hypotype, G.S.C. No. 10539: Member No. 2, Portage Chute Formation, South Knife River, locality 25299
Hypotype, G.S.C. No. 10888: Member No. 1, Portage Chute Formation, North Knife River, locality 25314

DESCRIPTION: Shape of corallum of northern Manitoba specimens appears to have been depressed hemispherical; at least 60 mm high with corresponding horizontal diameter of 160 mm. Corallites arranged in monoserial ranks, transverse exterior outline ranges from subrectangular to subelliptical, latter shape most common. Average corallite transverse length about 1.2 mm, corresponding width at mid-length and appressed ends 1.0 mm and 0.8 mm, respectively. Walls relatively thin and most not thickened at ends; total thickness of two appressed walls equal to, or slightly greater than, thickness of free wall. Consequently, transverse interior outline very similar to that of exterior. A few very short septal spines present.

Tabulae flat, variable in spacing, but relatively further apart than in most species: generally 3 tabulae occur in distance equal to 1½ times corallite mid-length width.

Lacunae tend to be approximately equidimensional and vary in transverse outline from subcircular to subelliptical. Vermiform lacunae rare. In most specimens 6–10 corallites arranged about subcircular lacunae, and 10–15 about elliptical ones. Diameter of most lacunae not more than 5 mm, and generally about 3 mm.

DISCUSSION: The most characteristic features of this easily recognizable species are the thin-walled, subelliptical corallites, not noticeably thickened at appressed ends, and the rather remarkably regularly shaped small lacunae. *Catenipora aequabilis* closely resembles *C. (Quepora) quebecensis*, and the two may be conspecific. The writer has compared Sinclair's (1955) specimen (G.S.C. No. 12385) of the latter species with Lowland specimens of *C. aequabilis*. The main difference noted is that walls are thinner and septa are present in most specimens of *C. aequabilis*.

Catenipora aequabilis has previously been described from the Ordovician of Baffin Island (Wilson, 1931) and Iglulik Island (Teichert, 1937). Wilson compared her species with *Halysites feildeni* but in the same publication also regarded it as a new species which she called *Halysites arcticus*. Unfortunately this name was placed only in a faunal list without further designation. Teichert (1937) pointed out that *H. arcticus* was a *nomen nudem* and accordingly named the species *H. aequabilis*. A specimen very probably belonging to this species was described by Miller and Youngquist (1947a) from the Ordovician of Sutton Island.

Catenipora agglomeratiformis (Whitfield)
(Pl. 14, figs. 10, 11)

1900 *Halysites agglomeratiformis* WHITFIELD, American Mus. Nat. Hist. Bull., v. 13, p. 20, Pl. 2, figs. 1, 2
1915 *Halysites agglomeratiformis* Whitfield. BASSLER, United States Nat. Mus. Bull. 92, v. 1, p. 584
1928 *Halysites agglomeratiformis* Whitfield. TROEDSSON, Medd. om Grønland, v. 72, p. 133, Pl. 46, figs. 1a–d
1937 [?] *Halysites rasmusseni* TEICHERT, Rept. Fifth Thule Exped., 1921–1924, v. 1, no. 5, p. 134, Pl. 9, figs. 5, 6; Pl. 10, fig. 2
1941 *Halysites agglomeratiformis* Whitfield. ROY, Field Mus. Nat. Hist. Geol. Mem., v. 2, p. 77, figs. 39a–c
1954 *Halysites agglomeratiformis* Whitfield. MILLER, YOUNGQUIST, and COLLINSON, Geol. Soc. America Mem. 62, p. 11, Pl. 8, fig. 1
1955 *Catenipora agglomeratiformis* (Whitfield). BUEHLER, Peabody Mus. Nat. Hist., Yale Univ. Bull. 8, p. 49
1955 [?] *Catenipora rasmusseni* (Teichert). BUEHLER, Peabody Mus. Nat. Hist., Yale Univ. Bull. 8, p. 65

OCCURRENCE: Portage Chute Formation: common in Member No. 1, North Knife River: locality 25313; and Member No. 2, South Knife River: localities 25295, 25296; and Churchill River: locality 25270

Hypotype, G.S.C. No. 10886: Member No. 2, Portage Chute Formation, South Knife River, locality 25295
Hypotype, G.S.C. No. 10889: Member No. 2, Portage Chute Formation, South Knife River, locality 25296

DESCRIPTION: In northern Manitoba, species represented by very well-preserved fragments of coralla, original shape of which is unknown. Corallites arranged in monoserial ranks, and most are constant in transverse outline and size. Typically length about 1.3 mm and corresponding width at mid-length and appressed ends 0.9 mm and 0.7 mm, respectively. Exterior and interior outline of each corallite very similar to that of *C. robusta* (Wilson), but corallite is smaller. Some forms assume nearly circular outline with diameter between 0.7 and 0.8 mm and are connected to those adjacent by attenuated elongated walls so that their appearance is not unlike that of *Halysites labyrinthica* (Goldfuss). Mesocorallites, however, absent in *C. agglomeratiformis*. No trace of septal spines seen.

Tabulae in most specimens flat and relatively widely spaced; typically three occur in distance equal to corallite mid-length width.

Lacunae very similar in transverse outline to those of *C. robusta* (Wilson) and *C. rubra* Sinclair and Bolton but much smaller. They vary in outline from subcircular to subvermiform, latter by far the most common. Individual lacunae rarely longer than 15 mm and have corresponding width of about 3 mm; most are about 10 mm long with width of 2 to 3 mm. They may curve gently, but few bend at angle of 90° or more.

DISCUSSION: This species was first described by Whitfield (1900) as Silurian from Princess Marie Bay in Ellesmere Island, where it was associated with *Receptaculites pearyi, Calapoecia borealis,* and *Heliolites perelegans.* According to Troedsson (1928, p. 133) these four species ". . . have been recognized together with a definitely older fauna at Cape Calhoun [and] there is no doubt that their real age is Ordovician." Troedsson's specimens of *C. agglomeratiformis* are from the *Halysites* limestone (lower part of the Cape Calhoun Series) of northern Greenland. Roy (1941), and Miller, Youngquist, and Collinson (1954) have also described it from the Ordovician of Silliman's Fossil Mount in southern Baffin Island.

Teichert (1937) described from the Silurian of King William Land a halysitid coral without mesocorallites which he called *Halysites rasmusseni.* The description and illustrations of *H. rasmusseni* suggest that it is *C. agglomeratiformis.* The only difference noted is that the lacunae do not appear to be so elongated as those in *C. agglomeratiformis.* It is not certain how significant this difference may be so that *H. rasmusseni* is here questionably placed under *C. agglomeratiformis.*

Catenipora foerstei sp. nov.

(Pl. 14, figs. 16, 17)

OCCURRENCE: Fairly common in Caution Creek Formation, in Member No. 1, Churchill River: locality 25282; and Upper Member, South Knife River: locality 25302

Holotype, G.S.C. No. 10892, paratype, G.S.C. No. 10893: locality 25302, South Knife River

DESCRIPTION: Corallites arranged in monoserial ranks some of which may be discontinuous. Transverse exterior outline of corallites similar to those of *C. robusta* (Wilson): subelliptical, and narrow ends flattened and appressed at junction of adjacent corallites. Size of most specimens constant: length 1.5 mm, and width at mid-length and appressed end 0.9 mm and 0.7 mm, respectively. Walls of many corallites remarkably thick and range between 0.2 and 0.3 mm. Transverse interior outline of most elliptical, more rarely subquadrate.

Tabulae flat and appear to vary in spacing: in most specimens 2–3 occur in distance equal to corallite mid-length width.

Lacunae large in relation to corallite size and rather variable in transverse outline. In one corallum subquadrate, subelliptical, and irregularly vermiform lacunae may occur together. Length of most does not exceed 15 mm; width 5 mm or less.

DISCUSSION: *Catenipora foerstei* is named in honor of the late Dr. August F. Foerste.

The species is similar to both *C. agglomeratiformis* (Whitfield) and *C. robusta* (Wilson). The transverse outlines of individual corallites are close to those of these two species but are intermediate in size: *C. agglomeratiformis* has smaller ones and *C. robusta* larger. The lacunae of the former species are also much smaller and are more regular in transverse outline. Those of *C. foerstei* attain nearly the same dimensions as those of *C. robusta.*

In most coralla of *C. foerstei,* some of the ranks tend to form an incomplete chain. In many, a gap equivalent to the length of one corallite is left between the end of one rank and the nearest adjacent one.

Catenipora sp.

OCCURRENCE: One specimen from Member No. 2 of the Chasm Creek Formation, Churchill River: locality 25287

DESCRIPTION: Specimen is small fragment of corallum. Corallites rather large, arranged in monoserial ranks, and have subelliptical transverse exterior outline. Average length about 2 mm, width at mid-length and appressed ends 1.5 mm and 1.0 mm, respectively. Walls relatively thin; slight thickening at outer parts of appressed walls gives elliptical outline to corallite interior.

Tabulae flat or slightly concave upward and relatively widely spaced: about 3 occur in distance equal to corallite mid-length width.

Lacunae vary in transverse outline from subpolygonal, (average diameter about 5 mm) to elongate-elliptical (average long diameter about 15 mm and short diameter about 2 mm). Ranks around this kind of lacuna tend to be subparallel and give corallum compressed appearance.

DISCUSSION: The specimen appears to be most closely related to *C. robusta* (Wilson). The corallites are very similar in shape to those of this species, but they tend to be consistently larger. Lacunae are narrower than in *C. robusta* and tend to have subparallel longer axes. The specimen may represent a new species, but until more complete coralla are found it is thought best not to assign it to any known species.

Genus *Manipora* Sinclair, 1955
Type Species: *Manipora amicarum* Sinclair, 1955
Manipora amicarum Sinclair
(Pl. 15, figs. 1–3)

1899 *Halysites catenularia* var. *gracilis* (Hall) [*partim*]. LAMBE, Geol. Surv. Canada Contr. Canadian
 Pal., v. 4, pt. 1, p. 69, Pl. 3, fig. 6(?)
1928 [?] *Halysites catenularia* (Linnaeus) [*partim*]. TWENHOFEL, Geol. Surv. Canada Mem. 154, p. 125
1944 *Halysites gracilis* (Hall) [*partim*]. LEITH, Jour. Pal., v. 18, no. 3, p. 268, Pl. 42, figs. 1, 2; Pl. 43,
 figs. 1(?), 3, 4
1947 *Halysites* spp. MILLER and YOUNGQUIST [*partim*], Jour. Pal., v. 21, no. 1, p. 5, Pl. 2, figs. 1, 2
1955 *Catenipora gracilis* Hall [*partim*]. BUEHLER, Peabody Mus. Nat. Hist., Yale Univ., Bull. 8,
 p. 36
1955 *Manipora amicarum* SINCLAIR, Trans. Roy. Soc. Canada, v. 49, sec. 4, p. 97, Pl. 1, figs. 1, 4, 10

OCCURRENCE: Fairly common in Member No. 2 of Portage Chute Formation, Nelson River: localities 25257, 25258; Churchill River: locality 25272; and South Knife River: localities 25296, 25299. Rare in Upper Member of Caution Creek Formation, South Knife River: locality 25303. Fairly common in Member No. 1 of Chasm Creek Formation, Churchill River: localities 25281, 25283; Member No. 2: localities 25286, 25289; and Member No. 3: locality 25290

Hypotype, G.S.C. No. 10373: Member No. 2, Portage Chute Formation, South Knife River, locality
 25296
Hypotype, G.S.C. No. 10374: Member No. 2, Portage Chute Formation, Churchill River, locality
 25272
Hypotype, G.S.C. No. 10375: Member No. 3, Chasm Creek Formation, Churchill River, locality
 25290

DESCRIPTION: Northern Manitoban specimens large, depressed hemispheric coralla in which many ranks have corallites arranged in multiple rows so as to give favositoid appearance to colony. Within corallum ranks may consist of monoserial to hexaserial rows of corallites. In transverse outline individual corallites large, polygonal, generally 5- to 6-sided, and have average "diameter" of 1.5–2 mm.

Tabulae flat and relatively closely spaced: about 3 occur in corallite diameter in young stages, and 3–4 in mature stages.

Lacunae rather variable in both transverse size and outline. In coralla that have corallites arranged in monoserial and biserial ranks lacunae relatively large and vary from subcircular to vermiform. Subcircular lacunae may have diameters of 10–15 mm, and vermiform lacunae long diameter as much as 40 mm and corresponding width of 5–10 mm. Where corallites arranged in ranks having numerous rows of corallites, lacunae tend to be subcircular and diameter ranges between 5 and 10 mm.

DISCUSSION: The writer has compared the holotype, and the Selkirk (= Dog Head) specimen illustrated by Leith (1944, Pl. 43, fig. 4) with the northern Lowland material. About the only noticeable difference is that most corallites of Selkirk specimens are slightly larger.

Manipora irregularis (Teichert)
(Pl. 14, figs. 12, 13)

1937 *Halysites irregularis* TEICHERT, Rept. Fifth Thule Exped., 1921–1924, v. 1, no. 5, p. 132, Pl. 7,
 figs. 4, 5; Pl. 8, fig. 3

1955 *Catenipora irregularis* (Teichert). BUEHLER, Peabody Mus. Nat. Hist., Yale Univ., Bull. 8, p. 64

OCCURRENCE: Rare in Member No. 2 of Portage Chute Formation, Nelson River: locality 25257; and Churchill River: locality 25272. Rare in rubble of Member No. 1, Chasm Creek Formation, Churchill River: locality 25283

Hypotype, G.S.C. No. 10560: Member No. 2, Portage Chute Formation, Nelson River, locality 25257
Hypotype, G.S.C. No. 10894: Member No. 1, Chasm Creek Formation, Churchill River, locality 25283

DESCRIPTION: Teichert's (1937) diagnosis of species as follows:

"Corallum massive; corallites irregularly subcylindrical. In places the corallites are very close together as in *Favosites*, in other places in the same individual they are arranged in short rows forming narrow meshes. The cross-section of the corallites depends upon their mode of occurrence. Where the corallites are closely spaced, they are pentagonal to hexagonal in cross-section; where they are arranged in rows the cross-section is subquadrangular to rounded. The diameter of the corallites is fairly constant and measures about 1.5 mm., but slightly larger and slightly smaller corallites are to be found. The tabulae are straight and there are seven to nine of them in a distance of 5 mm. Septal spines are usually absent, but are present in a few of the corallites. Their number appears to be twelve. Tubuli are absent."

Northern Manitoban specimens very similar to primary types illustrated from Ordovician of King William Land. Corallites arranged in exceedingly meandrine, closely spaced, often discontinuous ranks. Where uncrowded most corallites assume subcircular transverse outline and are somewhat produced toward narrow appressed walls. Diameter 1.2 mm–1.5 mm. Where crowded, they have polygonal outline and favositoid appearance and individual diameter about same as that of more circular forms. Walls very thin, as in *M. feildeni*.

Tabulae flat, thin, relatively closely spaced: about 3–4 occur in distance equal to corallite mid-length width.

Most lacunae very small and, because of meandrine nature of ranks, exceedingly irregular in transverse outline.

DISCUSSION: *Manipora irregularis* is very closely related to *M. feildeni* (Etheridge), and it may be a variety of that species. The main difference between the two is that *M. irregularis* has much more meandrine ranks and closely spaced corallites than *M. feildeni*. Corallites are larger, and the majority tend to have a polygonal or subpolygonal outline.

The stratigraphic position of hypotype No. 10894 is uncertain. The specimen was collected at river level from rubble presumably derived from Member No. 1 of the Chasm Creek Formation, but it may have been carried by river ice from outcrops of the Portage Chute Formation. The lithology of the specimen, however, suggests the former formation.

Manipora feildeni Etheridge
(Pl. 14, figs. 14, 15)

1878 *Halysites catenulatus* var. *Feildeni* ETHERIDGE, Quart. Jour. Geol. Soc. London, v. 34, p. 582, Pl. 28, fig. 1
1899 [?] *Halysites catenularia* var. *gracilis* (Hall) [*partim*]. LAMBE, Geol. Surv. Canada Contr. Canadian Pal., v. 4, pt. 1, p. 69, p. 74 (specimen 6), Pl. 3, fig. 7
1915 *Halysites catenularia feildeni* (Etheridge). BASSLER, United States Nat. Mus. Bull. 92, v. 1, 586
1925 [*non*] *Halysites catenularia feildeni* (Etheridge). HUME, Geol. Surv. Canada Mem. 145, p. 38, Pl. 8, fig. 3
1926 [?] *Halysites cylindricus* WILSON, Geol. Surv. Canada Bull. 44, Geol. Ser. 46, p. 15, Pl. 2, figs. 6, 7
1928 *Halysites feildeni* (Etheridge). TROEDSSON, Medd. om Grønland, v. 72, p. 132, Pl. 41; Pl. 42; Pl. 43, figs. 1a, b
1944 [?] *Halysites gracilis* (Hall) [*partim*]. LEITH, Jour. Pal., v. 18, no. 3, Pl. 43, fig. 2
1947 *Halysites* spp. MILLER and YOUNGQUIST [*partim*], Jour. Pal., v. 21, no. 1, p. 5, Pl. 1, fig. 3
1955 *Halysites feildeni* (Etheridge). BUEHLER, Peabody Mus. Nat. Hist., Yale Univ., Bull. 8, p. 43

OCCURRENCE: Fairly common in Member No. 2 of Portage Chute Formation, Nelson River: localities 25254, 25258; Churchill River: localities 25270, 25272, 25276; and South Knife River: locality 25299

Hypotypes, G.S.C. No. 10353, 10357: Nelson River, localities 25258, 25254, respectively

DESCRIPTION: Etheridge's (1878, p. 582) original description of *M. feildeni* as follows:

"Corallum massive; base concentrically and irregularly rugose; the corallites radiate horizontally from the centre of the base (resembling in habit those of *Favosites*), and then assume the vertical growth when at or near the outer edge of the corallum; tabulae thick and very closely arranged, which on weathering, gives a very rugose appearance to the corallites; reticulations between the chain like pattern on the upper surface of the corallum very small and polygonal; calices either elliptical or polygonal; and frequently only two or three corallites occur in a space or vertical wall constituting the reticulations."

Northern Manitoban specimens very well preserved and show considerable variation in shape and pattern of corallites. Most corallites in monoserial, discontinuous, irregularly meandrine ranks, but at junction of neighboring ranks, where crowded, many assume favositoid pattern. Transverse exterior outline of corallites variable within single corallum. Where arranged in monoserial rows they may have subcircular, subelliptical, or more rarely subquadrate outline. Subelliptical corallites most common and 1.1 mm long and correspondingly 0.9 mm and 0.7 mm wide, respectively, at mid-length and appressed ends. Where crowded most have polygonal outlines and average diameters of about 1.0 mm. Walls exceedingly thin in comparison with size of corallite, and consequently transverse interior very similar to exterior outline.

Tabulae nearly flat and variable in spacing: in most specimens 3–4 occur in distance equal to corallite mid-length width.

Lacunae exceedingly irregular in transverse outline and size and many continuous with those adjacent because of commonly discontinuous corallite ranks. Nearly all have small dimensions so that most neighboring ranks are close to one another and give corallum crowded appearance. Not many individual lacunae longer than 10 mm, and most less than 5 mm in width or length.

DISCUSSION: At the type locality at Cape Hilgard on Ellesmere Island *M. feildeni* is associated with the Ordovician *Receptaculites arcticus* and *Maclurites magna*. Etheridge (1878), Bassler (1950, p. 76), and Buehler (1955, p. 43–44), however, considered the strata in which it occurred to be Silurian, but Troedsson (1928, p. 133), on the basis of associated fauna at the type locality and the occurrence of the species in the Cape Calhoun Series of northern Greenland, stated that its age was Ordovician. The finding of *M. feildeni* in the Ordovician of northern Manitoba verifies Troedsson's conclusion.

Lambe (1899, Pl. 3, fig. 7) and Leith (1944, Pl. 43, fig. 2) figured a specimen from Port Churchill Manitoba, which they referred to *H. gracilis* Hall. The illustration is a drawing, and hence it is uncertain if features reproduced are accurate. The corallite size and pattern, however, suggest that it may be *M. feildeni*. The only difference noted (which may be caused by inaccuracies in drawing) is that nearly all the corallites are polygonal.

Wilson's (1926) *Halysites cylindricus* from the Beaverfoot Formation of British Columbia may be *M. feildeni*. The writer has examined the holotype and was impressed with its similarity with the latter species. Until more nearly complete specimens are available, however, it is best not to definitely place it in *M. feildeni*.

The specimen from the Silurian of the Lake Timiskaming area which Hume (1925) referred to *M. feildeni* does not belong in this species. The writer has examined it and found that well-developed mesocorallites are present.

There appears to be little evidence for Buehler's (1955) assumption that *M. feildeni* belongs in the genus *Halysites* (*s.s.*) and thus has mesocorallites. Etheridge's (1878) illustrations suggest that mesocorallites are absent.

Class GRAPTOLITHINA Bronn
Order DENDROIDEA Nicholson
Family DENDROGRAPTIDAE Roemer
Genus *Desmograptus* Hopkinson, 1875
Type Species: *Dictyograptus cancellatus* Hopkinson, 1875
Desmograptus canadensis (Whiteaves)
(Pl. 17, fig. 3)

1897 *Inocaulis Canadensis* WHITEAVES, Geol. Surv. Canada Pal. Foss., v. 3, pt. 3, p. 149, Pl. 17, fig. 4
1908 *Dictyonema canadense* (Whiteaves). RUEDEMANN, New York State Mus. Mem. 11, p. 131
1915 *Dictyonema canadense* (Whiteaves). BASSLER, United States Nat. Mus. Bull. 92, v. 1, p. 422
1947 *Dictyonema canadense* (Whiteaves). RUEDEMANN, Geol. Soc. America Mem. 19, p. 167, Pl. 30, fig. 5

OCCURRENCE: One specimen (hypotype, G.S.C. No. 10517) from Lower Member of Caution Creek Formation, South Knife River: locality 25304

DISCUSSION: The type specimen is from the Cat Head Member of the Red River Formation, southern Manitoba. The writer is of the opinion that the species should be placed in the genus *Desmograptus* which is "distinguished from *Dictyonema* by its undulating, anastomosing branches, only rarely connected by dissepiments." (Bulman, 1938, p. 17). Both Whiteaves' specimen and the hypotype fit the description of *Desmograptus* very well. The drawing of the type specimen illustrated by Whiteaves (1897) and Ruedemann (1947) does not show the anastomosing effect of the branches, nor the true width of the stipes.

Phylum MOLLUSCA Cuvier
Class GASTROPODA Cuvier
Subclass ANISOPLEURA Lankester
Superorder PROSOBRANCHIA Milne-Edwards
Order ARCHAEOGASTROPODA Thiele
Family TROCHONEMATIDAE Ulrich
Genus *Trochonema* Salter, 1859
Type Species: *Pleurotomaria umbilicata* Hall, 1847
Trochonema coxi Wilson
(Pl. 16, fig. 5)

1897 *Trochonema umbilicatum* (Hall). WHITEAVES, Geol. Surv. Canada Pal. Foss., v. 3, pt. 3, p. 198
1928 *Trochonema umbilicatum* (Hall). WILSON (*in* Soper), Geol. Surv. Canada Mus. Bull. 53, p. 126
1928 *Trochonema* sp. aff. *umbilicatum* (Hall). HUSSEY, Contr. Mus. Pal., Univ. Michigan, v. 3, no. 3, p. 74, Pl. 2; Pl. 2, figs. 5, 7
1928 *Trochonema umbilicatum* (Hall). TROEDSSON, Medd. om Grønland, v. 72, p. 22, Pl. 9, fig. 2; Pl. 10, figs. 2a, b
1938 *Trochonema coxi* WILSON, Trans. Roy. Soc. Canada, v. 32, sec. 4, p. 33, Pl. 3, figs. 1–4
1941 *Trochonema* sp., aff. *umbilicatum* (Hall). ROY, Field Mus. Nat. Hist., Geol. Mem., v. 2, p. 121, fig. 87
1954 *Trochonema* cf. *T. umbilicatum* (Hall). MILLER, YOUNGQUIST, and COLLINSON, Geol. Soc. America Mem. 62, Pl. 17, figs. 11, 12

OCCURRENCE: Common in Member No. 1 of Portage Chute Formation, North Knife River: localities 25312, 25313, 25314, 25315; and in Member No. 2, Nelson, Churchill, and South Knife rivers: all areas of outcrop. Rare in Member No. 1 of Surprise Creek Formation, Churchill River: locality 25272. Common in Member No. 1 of Caution Creek Formation, Churchill River: all areas of outcrop; and in Upper Member, South Knife River: all areas of outcrop west of northward bend of this river. Common in Chasm Creek Formation, Nelson River: locality 25269; and in Members No. 1, No. 2 and No. 3 of this formation, Churchill River: all areas of outcrop

Hypotype, G.S.C. No. 10808: Member No. 1, Portage Chute Formation, North Knife River, locality 25314

DISCUSSION: Wilson's (1938, p. 33–34) diagnosis of *T. coxi* was as follows:

"Shell large, holotype not complete, measuring 2¼ inches at the largest diameter, height 1⅛ inches . . . One specimen . . . measures 2 inches. Whorls robust rapidly enlarging, the upper surface and the band having a tendency to obliquity in the more mature specimen, which in the cross section of the whorl produces an irregular hexagonal outline, with the broadest part towards the outer margin; umbilicus faintly defined by a subangular ridge, moderately open in broken specimens but mostly covered by the prolongation of the lip in mature specimens; spire comparatively low.

"All these forms have been called *Trochonema umbilicatum* in the Manitoba Red River fauna, but they differ from the typical Black River and Trenton species . . . in the more rapidly enlarging whorl and the longer lip over the umbilicus."

The description of Wilson's species was based on internal molds. Except for hypotype No. 10808, the present writer's specimens are also internal molds similar in shape to the holotype. The hypotype is a very well-preserved specimen nearly completely covered with altered shell material and broken off apically. A comparison of it with the holotype and hypotypes of *Trochonema umbilicatum* (Hall) illustrated by Knight (1941, Pl. 41, figs. 2a–e) shows it to be quite different. *Trochonema umbilicatum* has two shoulders: a small one adjacent to the suture and an outer large one. The last is relatively deeply concave outward and slopes rather strongly upward. *Trochonema coxi*, on the other hand, appears to lack the smaller shoulder, and the larger one is only gently concave outward with a relatively low-angled slope. Growth lines on both species have nearly the same spacing and pattern.

Because internal molds from the Bad Cache Rapids and Churchill River groups all have approximately the same appearance, the writer is referring them to *T. coxi*. However, the stratigraphically higher specimens from the Churchill River Group may, in the future, be shown to belong to a different species if individuals with outer shell material are found.

The holotype of *T. coxi* is from the Ordovician of Akpatok Island, 450–600 feet above sea level. The species also occurs in the Dog Head and laterally equivalent Selkirk members of the Red River Formation, southern Manitoba. Wilson stated that the species was "...represented by a variety in the upper beds of the Stony Mountain horizon." Specimens that probably belong to *T. coxi* have been described by Troedsson (1928) from the Cape Calhoun Series of northern Greenland, and by Roy (1941), and Miller, Youngquist, and Collinson (1954) from Silliman's Fossil Mount in southern Baffin Island.

Genus *Holopea* Hall, 1847

Type Species: *Holopea symmetrica* Hall, 1847

Holopea gigantea sp. nov.

(Pl. 16, figs. 2, 3)

OCCURRENCE: Fairly common in Member No. 2 of Portage Chute Formation, Churchill and South Knife rivers: nearly all areas of outcrop.

Holotype, G.S.C. No. 10867, paratypes, G.S.C. No. 10868, 10869: Churchill River, localities 25272, 25275, 25271, respectively

DESCRIPTION: Shell large, consists of 4–4½ volutions having maximum diameter of 54 mm and estimated height of 45 mm. Apical angle approximately 85°. Whorls enlarge rapidly and evenly and are nearly circular in transverse outline: a slight concavity present near junction with adjacent whorls. Each covers about half of preceding whorl; last one forms little less than half height of shell. Umbilicus small, about 2½ mm wide where diameter of shell is 28 mm.

Above description based on holotype, which is largest specimen. Paratypes have about same proportions and considered immature individuals. Measurements as follows (estimated dimensions indicated):

Paratype	Maximum diameter (mm)	Height (mm)
10868	37	31 (est.)
10869	32	28 (est.)

DISCUSSION: *Holopea gigantea* appears to be most similar to *H. rotunda* Ulrich and Scofield but is larger.

Family PLEUROTOMARIIDAE d'Orbigny
Genus *Liospira* Ulrich and Scofield, 1897
Type Species: *Pleurotomaria micula* Hall, 1862
Liospira parva Wilson
(Pl. 16, figs. 4a, b)

1928 *Liospira* cf. *micula* (Hall). TROEDSSON, Medd. om Grønland v. 72, p. 16, Pl. 2, fig. 4
1938 *Liospira parva* WILSON, Trans. Roy. Soc. Canada, v. 32, sec. 4, p. 31, Pl. 1, figs. 1–3

OCCURRENCE: Fairly common in Member No. 1 of Caution Creek Formation, Churchill River: localities 25277, 25281, 25282; and rare in Upper Member, South Knife River: locality 25307

Hypotype, G.S.C. No. 10871: Member No. 1, Caution Creek Formation, Churchill River, locality 25282

DISCUSSION: Wilson (1938, p. 31–32) erected this species on internal molds of four specimens. Her description was as follows:

"Shell, small, most complete specimen 18 mm. in its largest diameter, and 7 mm. in height, having 4½ whorls present; spire very low but each whorl slightly below the preceding one; top of whorl flat but at the margin curving slightly down towards the slit band; lower side rounded; marginal angle more obtuse than is usual in the genus; umbilicus open and comparatively wide, measuring 7 mm. in the width of 18 mm.; aperture not preserved so that the degree of covering of the umbilicus by the lip is not evident; surface markings unknown."

The four Caution Creek specimens are internal molds, very similar to the holotype but larger. The largest (hypotype No. 10871) has an estimated 5½ whorls with a diameter of 28 mm and a height of 14 mm (estimated). Toward the outer volution the whorl tends to become angulated.

The holotype is from Akpatok Island at 800 feet above sea level, and the paratype from the "...red shales of the Stony Mountain horizon...". The latter horizon is now known as the Stony Mountain Shale Member [Gunn Member of Sinclair and Leith, 1958] of this formation.

Genus *Hormotoma* Salter, 1859
Type Species: *Murchisonia gracilis* Hall, 1847
Hormotoma winnipegensis Whiteaves
(Pl. 19, fig. 3)

1897 *Hormotoma Winnipegensis* WHITEAVES, Geol. Surv. Canada Pal. Foss., v. 3, pt. 3, p. 192, Pl. 21, fig. 1
1915 *Hormotoma winnipegensis* Whiteaves. BASSLER, United States Nat. Mus. Bull. 92, v. 1, p. 649
1938 *Hormotoma winnipegensis* Whiteaves. WILSON, Trans. Roy. Soc. Canada, v. 32, sec. 4, p. 31, Pl. 2, fig. 7
1941 [?] *Hormotoma rotundivolvis* ROY, Field Mus. Nat. Hist. Geol. Mem., v. 2, p. 111, fig. 78

OCCURRENCE: Common in Member No. 2 of Portage Chute Formation, Nelson, Churchill, and South Knife rivers: nearly all areas of outcrop

Hypotype, G.S.C. No. 10333: Nelson River, locality 25257

DESCRIPTION: Species represented by numerous internal molds. Largest, from South Knife River, attains estimated length of 160 mm and maximum diameter of 80 mm at outer whorl. Like Whiteaves' illustrated specimen it is laterally compressed. Hypotype No. 10333, best-preserved specimen in collection, uncompressed and has estimated (reconstructed) length of 130 mm and maximum diameter, at outer whorl, of about 75 mm.

DISCUSSION: Roy's (1941) holotype of *Hormotoma rotundivolvis*, from the Ordovician of Silliman's

Fossil Mount, Baffin Island, is very similar to immature *H. winnipegensis* from the Portage Chute Formation. Until more information is available on the Baffin Island species the present writer is questionably including it in the above synonymy.

Hormotoma winnipegensis was originally described from the Dog Head Member of the Red River Formation, southern Manitoba. Miller (1930, p. 199; 1932, p. 205) has listed a tentatively identified *H. winnipegensis* from the Lander Sandstone Member of the Bighorn Formation, Wyoming. Wilson (1938, p. 31) stated that the species also occurred in the Ordovician of Akpatok Island at "...sea-level and at 200 feet above sea-level...."

Family MACLURITIDAE Koken
Genus *Maclurites* Le Sueur, 1818
Type Species: *Maclurites magna* Le Sueur, 1818
Maclurites manitobensis (Whiteaves)

1890 *Maclurea Manitobensis* WHITEAVES, Trans. Roy. Soc. Canada, v. 7, sec. 4, p. 75, Pl. 12; Pl. 13 figs. 1, 2
1893 *Maclurea Manitobensis* Whiteaves. WHITEAVES, Canadian Rec. Sci., v. 5, p. 324
1897 *Maclurina manitobensis* (Whiteaves). ULRICH and SCOFIELD, Geol. Minnesota, v. 3, pt. 2, p. 1041, Pl. 76, figs. 4, 5; Pl. 82, fig. 45.
1897 *Maclurea (Maclurina) Manitobensis* Whiteaves. WHITEAVES, Geol. Surv. Canada Pal. Foss., v. 3, pt. 3, p. 194, Pl. 20, fig. 11
1900 *Maclurina manitobensis* (Whiteaves). SCHUCHERT, Proc. United States Nat. Mus., v. 22, p. 166
1915 *Maclurina manitobensis* (Whiteaves). BASSLER, United States Nat. Mus. Bull. 92, v. 2, p. 777
1928 *Maclurina manitobensis* (Whiteaves). TROEDSSON, Medd. om Grønland, v. 72, p. 21, Pl. 9, fig. 3; Pl. 7, fig. 2
1931 *Maclurina manitobensis* (Whiteaves). WILSON, Trans. Roy. Soc. Canada, v. 25, sec. 4, p. 300, Pl. 4, fig. 3
1937 *Maclurina manitobensis* (Whiteaves). TEICHERT, Rept. Fifth Thule Exped., 1921–1924, v. 1, no. 5, p. 74, Pl. 14, fig. 1; Pl. 15, fig. 2
1941 *Maclurina manitobensis* (?) (Whiteaves). ROY, Field Mus. Nat. Hist., Geol. Mem., v. 2, p. 115, fig. 81
1944 *Maclurites manitobensis* (Whiteaves). SHIMER and SHROCK, Index Fossils of North America, p. 469, Pl. 190, fig. 10
1947 *Maclurina* cf. M. *manitobensis* (Whiteaves). MILLER and YOUNGQUIST, Jour. Pal., v. 21, no. 1, p. 9, Pl. 6, figs. 3–5
1947 *Maclurina* cf. M. *manitobensis* (Whiteaves). MILLER and YOUNGQUIST, Jour. Pal., v. 21, no. 5, p. 412, Pl. 53, fig. 3; Pl. 54, figs. 3, 4
1954 *Maclurites manitobensis* (Whiteaves). MILLER, YOUNGQUIST, and COLLINSON, Geol. Soc. America Mem. 62, Pl. 12, figs. 1, 2; Pl. 13, figs. 1, 2

OCCURRENCE: Common in Member No. 1 of Portage Chute Formation, North Knife River: localities 25313, 25314, 25315; but rare on Churchill River: locality 25270. Abundant and characteristic of Member No. 2 of Portage Chute Formation, Nelson, Churchill, South Knife rivers: all areas of outcrop. Rare in Lower Member of Surprise Creek Formation, Nelson River: locality 25264

DISCUSSION: In identifying this species the writer has examined the type specimen from the Dog Head Member of the Red River Formation, and has followed Wilson's (1931, p. 300) detailed description of plesiotype No. 6510.

Numerous sections have been made of the northern Manitoba material, and these show that the specimens are definitely referable to *M. manitobensis*. Specimens vary from immature to full grown. The largest collected is 170 mm in diameter.

Maclurites manitobensis is very widespread and characteristic of the Red River Arctic fauna. In southern Manitoba it occurs in the Red River Formation. It is known as far north as northern Greenland where it occurs in the Cape Calhoun Series (Troedsson, 1928) and has been reported by Teichert (1937) from Melville Peninsula, Liddon Island, and northern Baffin Island. Roy (1941) and Miller, Youngquist, and Collinson (1954) have also described it from Silliman's Fossil Mount on southern Baffin Island. The latter authors stated (p. 14) that at the Mount "...large representatives of *Maclurites* are perhaps the most conspicuous fossils..." and occur in the upper limestone and dolomite zones. They identified two species from this zone. One is *M. manitobensis* (Whiteaves) and the other *M. triangularis* Teichert. Good summaries of the occurrence of *M. manitobensis* and other species in the Ordovician of the Arctic regions have been given by these authors.

Maclurites altus Wilson
(Pl. 16, fig. 6)

1928 cf. *Maclurina cuneata* (Whitfield). HUSSEY, Contr. Mus. Pal., Univ. Michigan, v. 3, no. 3, p. 73, Pl. 4, fig. 2
1928 *Maclurites* sp. A. WILSON (*in* Soper), Nat. Mus. Canada Bull. 53, p. 126
1931 *Maclurites altus* WILSON, Trans. Roy. Soc. Canada, v. 25, sec. 4, p. 302, Pl. 5, figs. 1, 2

OCCURRENCE: Rare in Member No. 2 of Portage Chute Formation. One specimen is from Nelson River: locality 25257; one (hypotype, G.S.C. No. 10884) from Churchill River: locality 25274; and one from South Knife River: locality 25299

DISCUSSION: Hypotype No. 10884 is the best preserved specimen. It is a somewhat laterally compressed internal mold containing approximately 3½ whorls. The maximum diameter is 113 mm and the depth 60 mm, and give a depth to diameter ratio of about 5/9. This ratio is very similar to that of 4/7 given by Wilson (1931) for the holotype.

Specimens referred to this species occur at numerous localities on Baffin Island in strata thought to be equivalent to the Red River Formation of southern Manitoba.

Maclurites ungava Wilson

1928 *Maclurites* n. sp. B. WILSON (*in* Soper), Geol. Surv. Canada Nat. Mus. Bull. 53, p. 126
1928 *Maclurites crassa* (Ulrich and Scofield). TROEDSSON, Medd. om Grønland, v. 72, p. 19, Pl. 3, fig. 4; Pl. 4, fig. 4; Pl. 9, fig. 1
1938 *Maclurites ungava* WILSON, Trans. Roy. Soc. Canada, v. 32, sec. 4, p. 33, Pl. 1, figs. 7–9

OCCURRENCE: Common and characteristic of Member No. 2 of Portage Chute Formation on Nelson and Churchill rivers: all areas of outcrop. No specimens, oddly enough, have been found on South and North Knife rivers.

DISCUSSION: Wilson's (1938, p. 33) description of this species is as follows:

"Shell moderate size, largest specimen, not complete, measuring 3 inches in its longest diameter; involutions lightly impressed; whorl enlarging less rapidly than usual on the flat surface but the perpendicular diameter of the lower convex side increasing very rapidly; marginal angle less acute than most species; sides convexly rounded to the umbilicus edge; umbilicus open, each whorl leaving the preceding one slightly revealed. The cross section of the whorl shows the width of the umbilicus is due to the position of its margin which is not perpendicularly over the preceding whorl as in most other described species but situated a little to the umbilicus side of its own centre, the section having a roughly triangular outline, slightly truncated at the line of contact with the preceding whorl.

"The species is similar to *M. crassa* Ulrich and Scofield, with which it has been frequently identified, in its open umbilicus and less rapidly enlarging flat surface. It differs from that species, however, in the much greater enlargement of the flat and convex aspects of the whorl."

Wilson's specimens were collected from the Ordovician strata at sea level on Akpatok Island, and from the Dog Head Member of the Red River Formation, southern Manitoba.

The Portage Chute specimens are very similar to the holotype but are larger. The largest has a diameter of 115 mm and a height on the outer whorl of 45 mm (estimated).

Order MESOGASTROPODA Thiele
Family SUBULITIDAE Miller
Genus *Fusispira* Hall, 1872
Type Species: *Fusispira ventricosa* Hall, 1872
Fusispira gigantea Wilson
(Pl. 16, fig. 1; Pl. 17, fig. 2)

1928 *Fusispira inflata* (Meek and Worthen) [*partim*]. TROEDSSON, Medd. om Grønland, v. 72, p. 23, Pl. 10, fig. 2; Pl. 11, fig. 1
1938 *Fusispira gigantea* WILSON, Trans. Roy. Soc. Canada v. 32, sec. 4, p. 35, Pl. 3, figs. 7, 8

1954 *Fusispira* sp. MILLER, YOUNGQUIST, and COLLINSON [*partim*], Geol. Soc. America, Mem. 62, p. 14, Pl. 16, fig. 9

OCCURRENCE: Rare in Member No. 1 of Portage Chute Formation, North Knife River: locality 25314. Fairly common in Member No. 2 of this formation, Nelson, Churchill, and South Knife rivers: nearly all areas of outcrop

Hypotype, G.S.C. No. 10360: Member No. 2, Portage Chute, Formation, South Knife River, locality 25299

Hypotype, G.S.C. No. 10361: Member No. 2, Portage Chute Formation, South Knife River, locality 25297

DISCUSSION: Wilson's (1938, p. 36) description of this species was as follows:

"A large robust form; 4 to 5 whorls in all, enlarging rapidly and uniformly each covering almost half of the preceding one. In the more complete of the two specimens found, the body whorl has a length of 2¼ inches, out of a total length of 3½ inches, lacking the tip of the spire and of the aperture; aperture wide and rounded at the bottom; canal, if present, less elongated than is usual in the genus.

"This form differs from any described species in its large size. Troedsson included it in *F. inflata* (Meek and Worthen) but it differs from that species not only in size but in its uniform and more rapid enlargement, its fewer whorls and its broader and more rounded aperture."

Among the numerous northern Manitoba specimens assigned to this species hypotype No. 10360 is best preserved. It is an internal mold about half a volution larger than the holotype. Its length is about 115 mm, and consists of at least 4½ whorls, the apical portion of which is missing. The maximum width is 62 mm.

Hypotype No. 10361 is even larger. Unfortunately it is not so well preserved as the first and is laterally compressed. Its length is about 138 mm and maximum width about 77 mm (measured at right angles to the direction of compression). It consists of about 3 whorls. The apex is missing.

Wilson's specimens were collected on Akpatok Island from Ordovician strata at sea level. The species also occurs in the Cape Calhoun Series of northern Greenland (Troedsson, 1928). Recently, Miller, Youngquist, and Collinson (1954) illustrated three specimens of *Fusispira* from the Ordovician of Silliman's Fossil Mount in southern Baffin Island. One of these (*see* synonymy) definitely appears to belong in *F. gigantea*.

Class CEPHALOPODA Leach
Order ENDOCERATIDA Teichert
Family ENDOCERATIDAE Hyatt
Genus *Cyclendoceras* Grabau and Shimer, 1910
Type Species: *Endoceras annulatum* Hall, 1847

In this genus are placed annulated orthoceraconic conchs. Annulations are well defined, subangular to rounded, and may be transverse or oblique to the conch axis.

Most sutures are nearly transverse to the conch axis.

The siphuncle is holochoanitic.

?Cyclendoceras kindlei Foerste

1892 *Endoceras annulatum* var. WHITEAVES, Trans. Roy. Soc. Canada, v. 9, sec. 4, p. 77, Pl. 5, figs. 1, 1a

1897 *Endoceras annulatum* Hall, var. WHITEAVES, Geol. Surv. Canada Pal. Foss., v. 3, pt. 3, p. 202

1929 *Cyclendoceras kindlei* FOERSTE, Denison Univ. Bull., Jour. Sci. Lab., v. 24, p. 152, Pl. 12, fig. 2; Pl. 22, fig. 2

OCCURRENCE: The type specimen was collected on Nelson River by Dr. Robert Bell in 1878, from beds here referred to Member No. 2 of Portage Chute Formation: locality 25257

DISCUSSION: Numerous internal molds of unannulated endoceratid cephalopods have been collected by the writer from the Portage Chute Formation on Nelson, Churchill, and South Knife rivers. The size and outline of many of these, as well as the pattern and spacing of the sutures is very similar to *C. kindlei*. Absence of surface annulations, however, precludes the possibility of positive identification.

Cyclendoceras belli sp. nov.
(Pl. 17, fig. 1; Pl. 18, figs. 1a, b)

OCCURRENCE: Two specimens from Caution Creek Formation. The holotype (G.S.C. No. 10516) is from Member No. 1, Churchill River: locality 25278. The other is from Upper Member, South Knife River: locality 25304

DESCRIPTION: Description of species based on holotype, well-preserved internal mold of phragmocone about 340 mm long.

Conch depressed dorsoventrally, elliptical in transverse outline, and enlarges from dorsoventral and lateral diameter of 42 mm and 70 mm, respectively, to corresponding measurements of 50 mm and 82 mm, 250 mm orad. Surface crossed by pronounced annulations spaced between 2 to 2½ times length of a camera and rising about 5 mm above intervening grooves. Tops of annulations sharply rounded, and intervening depressions broadly and uniformly concave. Annulations cross dorsal surface as broad interrupted "saddles", forming irregular nodes caused by their intersection with slightly lobed sutures and giving this side rather irregularly hummocky appearance. Depth of these "saddles" about equivalent to length of 3 camerae. On lateral sides, annulations sigmoidally curve strongly apicad at vertical angle of about 35° to conch axis and cross ventral surface as well-defined, uninterrupted "lobes", depth of which is about equal to length of 4 camerae.

Sutures approximately 6 mm apart, show little increase in adoral spacing, and are nearly transverse. They form shallow dorsal and ventral lobes, depth of which is between 1 and 1½ times length of camera.

Holotype sectioned transversely and longitudinally but shows no trace of septa or siphuncle.

DISCUSSION: The South Knife River specimen is a fragment preserving dorsal and lateral surfaces. It is about 120 mm long and has a lateral diameter of about 65 mm. Annulations are very similar in shape, spacing, and pattern to those of the holotype.

So far as the writer knows *C. belli* differs from all previously described species of this genus in having a nodose dorsal surface. All other species have uninterrupted annulations on this surface. *Cyclendoceras belli* is perhaps most similar to *C. popoagiense* Miller in its transverse outline, and size and spacing of the annulations but differs in that the annulations are more oblique.

The species is named in honor of Dr. Robert Bell, the first geologist to descend the Churchill River.

Genus *Parksoceras* Foerste and Savage, 1927
Type Species: *Orthoceras (Thoracoceras) lepidodendroides* Parks, 1915

This genus was erected for orthoceraconic conchs with the surface ornamented by nearly diagonally arranged mammaeform projections.

The genus is known from one species, *P. lepidodendroides*, and this, in turn, by two specimens: the hypotype, described below, and the holotype. No internal structures are present in either of these specimens. Both are compressed and, following Foerste and Savage's (1927) assumption, it is here considered that the dorsoventral diameter is shorter than the lateral.

Lack of information on internal structures makes the systematic position of this genus very uncertain, hence reference to the family Endoceratidae is open to question.

Parksoceras lepidodendroides (Parks)
(Pl. 31, fig. 2)

1913 *Orthoceras lepidodendroides* PARKS (*in* Tyrrell), Bur. Mines Ontario, 22nd Rept., pt. 1, p. 190
1915 *Orthoceras (Thoracoceras) lepidodendroides* Parks. PARKS, Trans. Roy. Canadian Inst., v. 11, p. 22, Pl. 2, fig. 4
1927 *Parksoceras lepidodendroides* (Parks). FOERSTE and SAVAGE, Denison Univ. Bull., Jour. Sci. Lab., v. 22, p. 45, Pl. 18, figs. 3A, B

OCCURRENCE: One specimen (hypotype, G.S.C. No. 10505) from the Upper Member of the Caution Creek Formation, South Knife River: locality 25304

DESCRIPTION: Hypotype about 170 mm in length, of which 90 mm belongs to phragmocone and remainder to living chamber. One side not preserved, and presumably remaining half dorsal with part of dorsolateral sides. Dorsoventral and lateral diameters 30 mm (estimated) and 42 mm, respectively, at most adapical portion. Approximately 40 mm above base of living chamber lateral diameter is 70 mm. Corresponding dorsoventral measurement cannot be estimated because of fragmentary nature of upper part of mold.

Surface of hypotype ornamented by mammaeform elevations having same arrangement and spacing as on type specimen. Because of weathering, however, not prominent.

Sutures more widely spaced than on holotype. There are 8 camerae in length of 80 mm compared with same number in 53 mm on type. Sutures form broadly rounded saddles on dorsal side, convexity of which equals depth of 1½ camerae. Saddles may have been formed by postdepositional compaction.

DISCUSSION: The holotype is from the Shamattawa Formation on Gods River, northern Manitoba.

Genus <i>Narthecoceras</i> Hyatt, 1895
Type Species: <i>Endoceras crassisiphonatum</i> Whiteaves, 1892

This genus is known only from siphuncles. They are orthoceraconic, and very weakly annulated, probably because of a slight enlargement of the segments between septa. The interior consists of fibrous calcareous deposits radiating from the center to exterior. There is a funnel-like cavity called the endosiphuncle which is open apically.

Three species have been referred to *Narthecoceras*, distinguished by the ratio of length of segment to its maximum dorsoventral diameter. Troedsson (1926, p. 32) gave the following ratios.

Narthecoceras simpsoni (Billings)	1/0.7 to 1/0.9
N. crassisiphonatum (Whiteaves)	1/1.2
N. inflatum Troedsson	1/1.5 to 1/1.6

The writer thinks that little emphasis should be placed on individual species of *Narthecoceras* in correlation until more information is available on extrasiphuncular structures. The genus and its contained species appear to be very artificial concepts.

Narthecoceras crassisiphonatum (Whiteaves)

1892 *Endoceras crassisiphonatum* WHITEAVES, Trans. Roy. Soc. Canada, v. 9, sec. 4, p. 79, Pl. 6, figs. 1–4; Pl. 7, fig. 1
1895 *Narthecoceras (Endoceras) crassisiphonatum* (Whiteaves). HYATT, American Geol., v. 16, p. 3
1897 *Endoceras (Narthecoceras) crassisiphonatum* Whiteaves. WHITEAVES, Geol. Surv. Canada Pal. Foss., v. 3, pt. 3, p. 204.
1905 *Endoceras crassisiphonatum* Whiteaves. RUEDEMANN, Bull. New York State Mus., v. 80, p. 300, fig. 1
1929 *Narthecoceras crassisiphonatum* (Whiteaves). FOERSTE, Denison Univ. Bull., Jour. Sci. Lab., v. 24, p. 188, Pl. 24, figs. 1A, B; Pl. 25, figs. 1, 2

OCCURRENCE: Fairly common in Member No. 2 of Portage Chute Formation, Churchill and Nelson rivers: most areas of outcrop. Rare in the Lower Member of Surprise Creek Formation, Nelson River: locality 25262. Rare in beds referred to the Upper Member of Caution Creek Formation, South Knife River: locality 25310

DISCUSSION: In southern Manitoba *N. crassisiphonatum* occurs in the Selkirk (= Dog Head) Member of the Red River Formation.

Order ACTINOCERATIDA
Family ACTINOCERATIDAE Saemann
Genus *Kochoceras* Troedsson, 1926
Type Species: *Kochoceras cuneiforme* Troedsson, 1926

This genus includes orthoceraconic conchs which tend to enlarge rather rapidly orad. The ventral wall is nearly flat, and the dorsal and lateral walls rounded in transverse outline. The lateral diameter of most specimens is larger than that of the dorsoventral.

Most sutures form rather deep, broadly rounded ventral lobes and shallow lateral saddles. Dorsal sutures may be transverse or weakly lobed. The new species *Kochoceras bailliei*, described below, however, differs from all species known to the writer in having fairly well-defined dorsal saddles.

The siphuncle is one of the most diagnostic structures of the genus. It is large in comparison to the conch diameter, and tends to decrease in relative size orad. Siphuncle segments are nummuloidal, ventrally flattened, and nearly in contact with the ventral wall.

Kochoceras bailliei sp. nov.

(Pl. 21, figs. 2a–c)

OCCURRENCE: Three specimens from Chasm Creek Formation, Churchill River. The holotype (G.S.C. No. 10865) is from Member No. 1: locality 25281; the paratype (G.S.C. No. 10866) from Member No. 2: locality 25285; and the third specimen from Member No. 3: locality 25290.

DESCRIPTION: Three specimens referred to this species are phragmocones, incomplete both adapically and adorally.

Holotype best preserved, about 126 mm long and contains estimated 12–13 camerae. Phragmocone enlarges from dorsoventral and lateral diameter of 35 mm and 67 mm respectively to corresponding measurements of 40 mm and 97 mm about 90 mm farther orad. Dorsal side broadly and uniformly convex and becomes strongly curved laterally. Maximum convexity closer to ventral than to dorsal side. Ventral side has slightly concave longitudinal zone along middle. Width of zone, at any one position, about half corresponding lateral diameter.

Sutures show no noticeable increase in spacing over length of phragmocone: about 11 mm apart on ventral and dorsal surfaces, and about 7–8 mm on lateral ones. They form well-defined ventral lobes, depth of which about equals that of two camerae. Toward ventrolateral surfaces they curve upward into very weak lateral saddles, and continue upward, with gentle curvature, over dorsal side forming shallow but well-defined dorsal saddles. In dorsoventral section septa very weakly curved and oblique to long axis of phragmocone making vertical angle of about 55° with it.

Siphuncle has maximum dorsoventral diameter of 15 mm where corresponding measurement of phragmocone is 35 mm. Where latter measurement is 40 mm dorsoventral and lateral diameters of siphuncle are 20 mm and 43 mm, respectively. Ventral surface of siphuncle flattened and about 2 mm from conch wall. Dorsal surface better preserved than ventral, but because of preservation, structure of septal necks and connecting rings cannot be definitely ascertained. Their pattern, however, appears similar to that of *K. cuneiforme* Troedsson (Troedsson, 1926, Pl. 37, fig. 2), with neck recurved so that it almost parallels septum and continues with little change in curvature on to connecting ring. Latter strongly arched, and lower part almost parallels septum at area of adnation.

Paratype longer than holotype. It is about 205 mm long and enlarges from dorsoventral and lateral diameter of 25 mm (estimated) and 60 mm, respectively, near base of phragmocone, to corresponding measurements of 38 mm and 92 mm, about 110 mm further orad.

Sutures have same spacing and pattern as on holotype.

DISCUSSION: In its rate of enlargement and transverse shape *Kochoceras bailliei* appears closest to the specimen from Silliman's Fossil Mount which Roy (1941, p. 138–140) called *K. troedssoni*. Miller, Youngquist, and Collinson (1954, p. 72–74) referred this specimen to *K. cuneiforme* Troedsson. *Kochoceras bailliei* differs from the Baffin Island individual and, as far as the writer knows, from all previously described species of *Kochoceras* in the presence of fairly well defined dorsal saddles.

The species is named in honor of Dr. A. D. Baillie.

Kochoceras giganteum sp. nov.

(Pl. 19, fig. 1)

OCCURRENCE: One specimen (holotype, G.S.C. No. 10864) from Member No. 3 of Chasm Creek Formation, Churchill River: locality 25290

DESCRIPTION: Holotype rather poorly preserved phragmocone about 300 mm long, incomplete both adapically and adorally. Only one side and part of lateral margins preserved. Because preserved side is nearly flat it is considered ventral.

Phragmocone enlarges from dorsoventral and lateral diameters of 40 mm and 68 mm, respectively, to corresponding estimated measurements of 58 mm and 120 mm about 100 mm farther orad. Only one lateral side preserved farther orad. Its outline suggests constant lateral rate of expansion throughout shell. Thus, at farther orad distance of 112 mm estimated dorsoventral and lateral diameters should be approximately 70 mm and 190 mm, respectively. Restored transverse outline probably compressed-oval, and ventral side nearly flat along middle and curving rather sharply upward ventrolaterally to join dorsal with narrowly curved lateral margin.

Sutures, where preserved, show no pronounced orad change in spacing along ventral side. They are 11–13 mm apart and form deep ventral lobes, depth of which about equals that of 2 camerae. Adorally weak ventral saddle appears to form on lobe. Base of specimen broken off at septum which is deeply concave both dorsoventrally and laterally. Depth of curvature about 15 mm and 40 mm, respectively. In dorsoventral profile maximum curvature of this septum is closer to ventral than to dorsal side.

Details of siphuncle not preserved.

DISCUSSION: *Kochoceras giganteum* differs from nearly all previously described species of the genus in its rapid rate of lateral enlargement and large size. *Kochoceras grande* Foerste from the Lander Sandstone Member of the Bighorn Formation of Wyoming is nearly as large but tapers less.

Kochoceras sp. I

1947b *Kochoceras* spp. MILLER and YOUNGQUIST [*partim*], Jour. Pal., v. 21, no. 5, p. 418, Pl. 57, fig. 1

OCCURRENCE: One specimen from Member No. 1 of Portage Chute Formation, North Knife River: locality 25314

DISCUSSION: The specimen is a very poorly preserved internal sandstone mold of a phragmocone from the same locality as the one illustrated by Miller and Youngquist (*see* synonymy). It is identical with the latter in nearly every essential respect but is shorter. Because of the poor state of preservation the writer does not think it advisable to refer it to any previously described species.

Miller and Youngquist (1947b) stated that their specimen was collected from dolomite along the North Knife River. Field work has shown, however, that it is in all probability from the sandstone member (No. 1) of the Portage Chute Formation and not from the overlying dolomitic limestone member (No. 2).

Kochoceras sp. II

OCCURRENCE: One specimen from Member No. 2 of Red Head Rapids Formation, Churchill River: locality 25293

DESCRIPTION: Specimen very poorly preserved phragmocone approximately 130 mm long, incomplete adapically and adorally. Estimated dorsoventral and lateral diameters 12 mm and 25 mm, respectively, at lower end. About 110 mm farther orad estimated diameters 35 mm and 46 mm. Dorsal side broadly rounded. Ventral side nearly flat in middle and curves rather rapidly ventrolaterally to join dorsal side so that transverse outline compressed-oval.

Sutures about 12 mm apart over surface. On dorsal side nearly transverse but ventrally form rather deep lobes the depth of which is equivalent to that of about 1½ camerae.

DISCUSSION: The relationships of this specimen are not clear. It appears to differ from most of those previously described in that the dorsoventral diameter is proportionally greater in relation to the lateral, and that lateral sides are not as rapidly expanding.

Family HURONIIDAE Foerste and Teichert
Genus *Huronia* Stokes, 1824
Type Species: *Huronia bigsbyi* Stokes, 1824

To the genus *Huronia* are referred large siphuncles in which the upper part of each connecting ring is annulated. The lower part is constricted, in most specimens occupies two-thirds to three-fifths of the length of the ring and may be cylindrical, or contracted gradually orad to present a concave outward appearance in outline.

Outer parts of septa are rarely preserved. Inner ends appear to be without distinct septal necks. Each septum arises adnate to the upper and inner surface of the annulation of the lower chamber, and continues adnate to the lower part of the connecting ring of the upper chamber. In most specimens it becomes free at the base of the annulation. Troedsson (1926, Pl. 2, fig. 5) has given an excellent illustration of siphuncle-septum relationship in *Huronia arctica* Troedsson.

Most representatives of the genus *Huronia* occur in Silurian rocks. Only three American Ordovician species are known to the present writer. Two of these—*H. arctica* Troedsson and *H. septata* Parks—occur high in the Ordovician. The other—*H. occidentalis* Foerste—is from the Red River Formation of Manitoba, and related rocks in Wyoming.

Huronia septata Parks

1915 *Huronia septata* Parks, Trans. Roy. Canadian Inst., v. 11, p. 27, Pl. 5, fig. 8
1924 *Huronia septata* Parks. Foerste, Contr. Mus. Geol., Univ. Michigan, v. 2, no. 3, p. 57, Pl. 8, fig. 1; Pl. 10, fig. 6
1927 *Huronia septata* Parks. Foerste and Savage, Denison Univ. Bull., Jour. Sci. Lab., v. 22, p. 71, Pl. 12, figs. 1, 2, 4
1936 *Huronia septata* Parks. Foerste and Cox, Geol. Mag., v. 73, no. 7, p. 302, Pl. 4, fig. 6
1943 [*non*] *Huronia* cf. *septata* Parks. Okulitch, Trans. Roy. Soc. Canada, v. 37, sec. 4, p. 64, Pl. 2, fig. 7

Occurrence: Rare in Chasm Creek Formation, Nelson River: locality 25269; and common in Member No. 3 of this formation, Churchill River: locality 25290

Description: One of Chasm Creek specimens contains part of ventral and ventrolateral conch wall. Septa, in specimen, rather deeply concave orad and sutures form broadly rounded ventral lobes. Siphuncle, which has maximum diameter of 43 mm at annulation, almost in contact with ventral wall and nearly circular in transverse outline. Radius of curvature of preserved part of conch wall estimated between 70 and 80 mm.

Discussion: *Huronia septata* appears to be a diagnostic fossil for the upper part of the Chasm Creek Formation. Other members of this species also occur high in the Ordovician. The type specimen is from the Shamattawa Formation of Gods River, Manitoba. Foerste and Cox (1936, p. 302) and Cox (1936, p. 29) have described the species from the Ordovician of Akpatok Island where it occurs 650 feet above sea level and is associated with *Aulacera undulata* (Billings). The last occurrence is interesting because the same association is found on Churchill River.

Family Gonioceratidae Hyatt
Genus *Lambeoceras* Foerste, 1917
Type Species: *Gonioceras Lambii* Whiteaves, 1891

The conch of this easily recognizable genus is straight. Adorally the lateral sides expand rapidly; the dorsoventral increase is more gradual. The most characteristic feature is the markedly dorsoventrally depressed conch. In transverse outline dorsal and ventral sides are rather gently convex, the latter less so than the former. Lateral sides may be acutely angular, subangular, or very narrowly rounded.

Sutures form broad dorsal and ventral lobes and narrowly rounded to subangular lateral saddles. Septa are rather deeply concave laterally, but gently concave to nearly flat dorsoventrally.

Troedsson (1926) has given excellent descriptions and illustrations of the siphuncle of *Lambeoceras*. It is relatively large, ventral, with short rather strongly curved septal necks and nummuloidal connecting rings.

Lambeoceras kronlundi Miller and Youngquist
(Pl. 32, fig. 1)

1926 [?] *Tripteroceras* (?) sp. ind. (*Cf. T. oweni* Clarke) Troedsson, Medd. om Grønland, v. 71, p. 44, Pl. 18, figs. 4, 5
1947b *Lambeoceras kronlundi* Miller and Youngquist, Jour. Pal., v. 21, no. 5, p. 416, Pl. 54, figs. 1, 2

Occurrence: Common in Member No. 1 of Portage Chute Formation, North Knife River: locality 25313

Hypotype, G.S.C. No. 10332

DESCRIPTION: Holotype of *Lambeoceras kronlundi* internal sandstone mold of living chamber from same horizon and locality as present specimens. Latter also internal sandstone molds but more nearly complete than holotype, and some have partly preserved phragmocone.

Hypotype No. 10332 best preserved; about 70 mm in length, measured along median-ventral side, of which about 45 mm belongs to living chamber and remainder to phragmocone. Latter has 5 camerae. Lowest part of specimen has dorsoventral and lateral diameters of 18 mm and 35 mm, respectively, and enlarges orad to corresponding estimated measurements of 27 mm and 50 mm at preserved top of living chamber. Dorsal side more convex than ventral, and lateral margins rather roundly angulated.

Sutures about 5 mm apart throughout length of phragmocone and form dorsal and ventral lobes and narrowly rounded lateral saddles. Bottoms of lobes about 1–1½ camerae below tops of corresponding saddles. Septa concave laterally but only slightly so dorsoventrally.

Largest specimen collected nearly complete living chamber with one camera adhering. Chamber about 90 mm long and enlarges from dorsoventral and lateral diameters of 27 mm and 48 mm, respectively, at base to corresponding estimated dimensions of 30 mm and 60 mm at preserved top. It has approximately same adoral rate of expansion as phragmocones of other specimens. Lateral sides appear to become more rounded orad.

No trace of siphuncle found in any of specimens.

DISCUSSION: Troedsson (1926) illustrated a living chamber from the Cape Calhoun Series of northern Greenland, which he referred to *Tripteroceras* (?) sp. indet. The appearance of his specimen is very similar to that of *Lambeoceras kronlundi* so that the present writer is questionably placing it in synonymy.

Lambeoceras nudum Troedsson

1926 *Lambeoceras nudum* TROEDSSON, Medd. om Grønland, v. 71, p. 47, Pl. 17, figs. 3, 4; Pl. 22

OCCURRENCE: Four specimens from Caution Creek Formation. Two are from Member No. 1: Churchill River: localities 25280, 25282; and two from the Upper Member, South Knife River: locality 25304

Hypotype, G.S.C. No. 10536: locality 25304

DESCRIPTION: Hypotype No. 10536, most complete specimen collected, internal mold about 240 mm in length of which about 50 mm belongs to living chamber and remainder to phragmocone. Latter has about 27 preserved camerae. Dorsoventral diameter 33 mm and lateral 84 mm at 20 camerae (140 mm) below living chamber. At base of chamber two measurements 40 mm (estimated) and 95 mm, respectively. Dorsal side slightly more convex than ventral, and lateral margins acute in transverse outline.

Lowermost sutures about 6 mm apart on middle of dorsal and ventral sides and separation gradually increases to about 7 mm near living chamber. They form broad shallow ventral lobes which curve upward to lateral margins and form acute saddles. Dorsal lobes shallower than those on ventral. Sutures show little or no tendency to flatten toward lateral margins. Depth of ventral lobes below corresponding lateral saddles equal to that of about three camerae; on dorsal, depth about equivalent to two camerae. Septa concave laterally but nearly flat dorsoventrally.

DISCUSSION: The type specimen of *L. nudum* is from the Cape Calhoun Series of northern Greenland.

Lambeoceras landerense Foerste

1935 *Lambeoceras landerense* FOERSTE, Denison Univ. Bull., Jour. Sci. Lab. v. 30, p. 53, Pl. 6, fig. 1

OCCURRENCE: Two specimens from Member No. 2 of Portage Chute Formation. One (hypotype, G.S.C. No. 10535) is from South Knife River: locality 25299; the other from Churchill River: locality 25274

DESCRIPTION: Both specimens portions of phragmocones. Churchill River specimen contains approximately 23 camerae, and South Knife one about 17 camerae.

Churchill River specimen about 130 mm long. At dorsoventral diameter of 33 mm lateral diameter 90 mm. About 88 mm orad these diameters 37 mm and 114 mm, respectively. Dorsal side slightly more convex than ventral, and lateral margins acute.

Sutures 4–6 mm apart along middle of dorsal and ventral sides. They form broadly rounded ventral lobes which become flatter near lateral margins and form acute lateral saddles. Dorsal sutures nearly straight across middle and curve upward to lateral borders. Depth of ventral lobes below corresponding lateral saddles equal to that of about five camerae. On dorsal side depth equivalent to about 3½ camerae. Septa concave both laterally and dorsoventrally. Depth of curvature in this latter direction equivalent to depth of one camera. That of former direction could not be determined.

South Knife River specimen at about same growth stage as preceding one. Approximately 105 mm long. At dorsoventral diameter of 32 mm corresponding lateral diameter 99 mm. About 62 mm orad two diameters 38 mm and 116 mm (estimated), respectively. Sutures more widely spaced than on Churchill River specimen and average about 7–8 mm apart along median-dorsal and ventral side.

DISCUSSION: These two specimens are most similar to *Lambeoceras landerense* from the Lander Sandstone Member of the Bighorn Formation, Wyoming. They agree with it in having nearly the same spacing and curvature of sutures, bluntly rounded lateral margins, approximately the same ratios of dorsoventral to lateral diameters, and the same rates of lateral enlargement.

Lambeoceras baffinense Miller, Youngquist, and Collinson

1928 [?] *Gonioceras* (?) sp. (A) FOERSTE, Contr. Mus. Pal., Univ. Michigan, v. 3, p. 46, Pl. 1, fig. 4
1928 [?] *Gonioceras* (?) sp. (B) FOERSTE, Contr. Mus. Pal., Univ. Michigan, v. 3, p. 47, Pl. 5, fig. 4
1932 [?] *Lambeoceras* cf. *nudum* Troedsson. FOERSTE, Denison Univ. Bull., Jour. Sci. Lab., v. 27, Pl. 24, fig. 1
1937 [?] *Lambeoceras* cf. *L. lambei* (Whiteaves). TEICHERT, Rept. Fifth Thule Exped. 1921–1924, v. 1, no. 5, p. 98, Pl. 19, fig. 2
1937 [?] *Lambeoceras* cf. *L. nudum* Troedsson. TEICHERT, Rept. Fifth Thule Exped. 1921–1924, v. 1, no. 5, p. 98
1954 *Lambeoceras baffinense* MILLER, YOUNGQUIST, and COLLINSON, Geol. Soc. America Mem. 62, p. 79, Pl. 37, fig. 7; Pl. 38, figs. 1–3; Pl. 39, fig. 1; Pl. 40, fig. 1; Pl. 46, fig. 14

OCCURRENCE: Four specimens from Member No. 2 of Portage Chute Formation. Two are from Churchill River: locality 25275; and two from South Knife River: locality 25299

Hypotype, G.S.C. No. 10513: Churchill River: locality 25275

DESCRIPTION: Hypotype No. 10513 most complete specimen collected and almost identical to holotype. About 220 mm in length, measured along median-dorsal side, of which approximately 25 mm belongs to living chamber and remainder to phragmocone. Latter has about 29 preserved camerae. Dorsoventral diameter 17 mm and lateral 42 mm at 180 mm below living chamber. Specimen enlarges rapidly orad in lateral outline, and sides diverge at about 25°. Dorsoventral rate of enlargement gradual and uniform. At distance of 30 mm below living chamber estimated dorsoventral and lateral diameters 29 mm and 113 mm (estimated) respectively. Dorsal side slightly more convex than ventral. Lateral margins narrowly acute.

Adapically, camerae rather deep, 7–8 mm on average over middle of dorsal and ventral sides, whereas adorally they average 6–7 mm. Sutures form broadly rounded ventral lobes which do not flatten near lateral margins. On dorsal side sutures nearly horizontal over middle and curve rather steeply upward to lateral margins with little flattening. Adapical depth of ventral lobes about equal to that of 2 camerae and about 5 camerae adorally. Corresponding lobe depths at two positions on dorsal side 2 camerae and 4 camerae, respectively. Septa only slightly concave dorsoventrally.

DISCUSSION: Miller, Youngquist, and Collinson (1954) described this species from the limestone portion of Silliman's Fossil Mount in southern Baffin Island. They included questionably in synonymy, specimens previously described by Foerste, and by Teichert (1937) which came from the Putnam Highland of southwestern Baffin Island, and Mount Nautilus in the northern part of the island.

Lambeoceras walkeri sp. nov.
(Pl. 20, fig. 1)

OCCURRENCE: Two specimens (holotype, G.S.C. No. 10531; paratype, G.S.C. No. 10533) from Lower Member of Surprise Creek Formation, Nelson River: locality 25264

DESCRIPTION: Holotype more nearly complete specimen. Plaster cast has been made of it (plasto-holotype, G.S.C. No. 10532), and original sectioned for details of septa and siphuncle.

Holotype 119 mm in length, measured along median-dorsal side, of which 54 mm belongs to living chamber and remainder to phragmocone, which contains 6 camerae. Conch enlarges rather rapidly orad in lateral profile. Dorsoventral rate of increase not definitely known because of crushing, but does not appear large. At 3½ camerae (41 mm) below base of living chamber, measured along median-ventral side, dorsoventral diameter 23 mm, and corresponding lateral diameter 76 mm. These two dimensions are 19 mm and 103 mm, respectively, 21 mm above base of chamber. Former measurement probably too small because of dorsoventral compression. Dorsal and ventral sides appear equally convex, and lateral margins acute and narrowly rounded in transverse outline.

Camerae in holotype have approximately same depth, 9–11 mm along both median-dorsal and ventral sides. Sutures form deep ventral lobes and become nearly horizontal laterally and form acute lateral saddles. Dorsal lobes broader and shallower because of upward slope of septa from ventral to dorsal side. Bottoms of ventral lobes about 3 camerae below corresponding lateral saddles, and those of dorsal about 2 camerae. Septa very slightly curved in dorsoventral direction but strongly curved laterally.

Siphuncle very poorly preserved. Only septal necks present, and they show siphuncle was slightly ventrad. Where dorsoventral conch diameter is 22 mm, siphuncle, at passage through septum, is 8 mm wide. Its ventral side is about 5 mm from ventral conch wall. Necks bent abruptly and almost at right angles to septa, are about 3 mm long, nearly straight, and roughly parallel to dorsal and ventral conch walls.

Paratype more fragmentary and thought to be immature. Three camerae and part of living chamber preserved. Typical strong curvature of sutures present.

DISCUSSION: *Lambeoceras walkeri* can easily be distinguished from most species by the strong curvature of sutures. The most similar species, in this respect are *L. richmondensis* Foerste and *L. montrealense* Flower. Compared with *L. walkeri*, *L. richmondensis* from the Whitewater of Indiana has deeper camerae and enlarges more rapidly in lateral profile. *Lambeoceras montrealense*, from the Terrebonne Formation of Montreal, is smaller and much thicker.

The species is named in honor of Mr. D. W. Walker, the writer's field assistant during the season of 1951.

Family SACTOCERATIDAE Troedsson

Genus *Paractinoceras* Hyatt, 1900

Type Species: *Sactoceras Canadense* Whiteaves, 1892

Paractinoceras canadense (Whiteaves)

1892 *Sactoceras Canadense* WHITEAVES, Trans. Roy. Soc. Canada, v. 9, sec. 4, p. 85, Pl. 10, figs. 1a–c
1897 *Actinoceras (Sactoceras ?) Canadense* (Whiteaves). WHITEAVES, Geol. Surv. Canada Pal. Foss. v. 3, pt. 3, p. 210
1906 *Paractinoceras canadense* (Whiteaves). WHITEAVES, Geol. Surv. Canada Pal. Foss., v. 3, pt. 4, p. 344
1915 *Actinoceras (Paractinoceras) canadense* (Whiteaves). BASSLER, United States Nat. Mus. Bull. 92, v. 1, p. 11
1929 *Paractinoceras canadense* (Whiteaves). FOERSTE, Denison Univ. Bull., Jour. Sci. Lab., v. 24, p. 210, Pl. 14, fig. 2; Pl. 26, figs. 3a, b
1932 *Paractinoceras canadense* (Whiteaves). MILLER, Trans. Connecticut Acad. Arts and Sci., v. 31, p. 265, Pl. 21, fig. 4
1935 *Paractinoceras canadense* (Whiteaves). FOERSTE, Dension Univ. Bull., Jour. Sci. Lab., v. 30, p. 57, Pl. 11, fig. 5
1942 *Paractinoceras canadense* (Whiteaves). MILLER and CARRIER, Jour. Pal., v. 16, no. 5, p. 544, Pl. 78, figs. 4, 5
1954 *Paractinoceras canadense* (Whiteaves). MILLER, YOUNGQUIST, and COLLINSON, Geol. Soc. America Mem. 62, p. 65, Pl. 29, figs. 1–3

OCCURRENCE: Rare in Member No. 2 of Portage Chute Formation, Churchill River: locality 25272
DISCUSSION: The holotype of *P. canadense* is from the Dog Head Member of the Red River

Formation, southern Manitoba. The species has also been reported from the Lander Sandstone and the middle dolomite member of the Bighorn Formation, Wyoming, and from the Ordovician of Silliman's Fossil Mount, Baffin Island.

Paractinoceras(?) *churchillense* sp. nov.

(Pl. 20, fig. 3; Pl. 29, fig. 3)

OCCURRENCE: One specimen (holotype, G.S.C. No. 10534) from Member No. 2 of Chasm Creek Formation, Churchill River: locality 25287

DESCRIPTION: Holotype internal mold about 270 mm long, of which approximately 85 mm belongs to living chamber and remainder to phragmocone. Phragmocone, incomplete adapically, has estimated 18–19 preserved camerae. In lateral profile specimen enlarges gradually orad to base of living chamber, where walls become approximately parallel. Orad dorsoventral increase in diameter also gradual. Conch subelliptical in transverse outline; lateral diameter is longer. Ventral side less convex than dorsal. At about 170 mm, or 17 camerae, below base of living chamber, dorsoventral and lateral diameters 28 mm and 48 mm, respectively. Corresponding two dimensions at base of this chamber 42 mm (estimated) and 63 mm and at preserved top of chamber 43 mm (estimated) and 63 mm, respectively.

Sutures form broad dorsal and ventral lobes and narrowly rounded saddles. Heights of saddles above corresponding lobes approximately equal to depth of one camera. Sutures about 7 mm apart apicad and 13 mm orad. Those of uppermost camera only 9 mm apart and suggest mature specimen. Septa concave laterally but have little curvature dorsoventrally.

Dorsoventral section showed only faint traces of siphuncle, which seems ventrad of center.

DISCUSSION: In its shape and pattern of sutures the Churchill River specimen appears closest to *Paractinoceras*. The generic position must be considered uncertain until the siphuncle is known. The only previously known species, *P. canadense*, is much smaller.

Order MICHELINOCERATIDA Flower

Family STEREOPLASMOCERATIDAE Kobayashi

Genus *Gorbyoceras* Shimizu and Obata, 1935

Type Species: *Orthoceras gorbyi* Miller, 1894

Flower (1946, p. 143–145) has given a detailed discussion of this genus. His diagnosis is as follows:

". . . annulated shells with longitudinal markings of the external aspect of *Spyroceras* which vary widely in details of the annulations and the surface features, but agree in having a subcentral siphuncle composed of cyrtochoanitic segments."

Gorbyoceras giganteum sp. nov.

(Pl. 18, fig. 2; Pl. 25, figs. 1, 3)

OCCURRENCE: One specimen (holotype, G.S.C. No. 10525) from Member No. 2 of Chasm Creek Formation, Churchill River: locality 25285

DESCRIPTION: Holotype fairly well preserved internal mold, incomplete adapically and adorally. Approximately 460 mm in length, of which about 145 mm belongs to living chamber and remainder to phragmacone. Specimen elliptical in transverse outline, and dorsoventral diameter the longer. About 240 mm below base of living chamber dorsoventral diameter 53 mm and lateral diameter 43 mm (estimated). (These and the following measurements are made on top of annuli.) Orad, lateral sides expand very gradually to about second annulus above living chamber where they contract asymmetrically. Dorsal side nearly straight up to base of living chamber, but ventral gently convex, and maximum curvature occurs about two–three camerae below living chamber. Dorsal and ventral sides contract rather evenly above base of chamber. In lateral profile, however, one lateral side nearly straight, whereas opposite one curves inward above base of living chamber to give this profile an asymmetrical aspect. Because of this asymmetry annuli are no longer transverse as they are on phragmocone but slope progressively upward from nearly straight lateral to curved side. At base of living chamber, dorsoventral and lateral diameters 72 mm and 59 mm, respectively; 100 mm above this base corresponding measurements 62 mm and 47 mm.

Annuli transverse on phragmocone but rise on living chamber from one of lateral sides to other so that uppermost annulus makes horizontal angle of about 25°. Throughout specimen they are rather sharply rounded and separated by concave interspaces. On phragmocone, tops of annuli about 15 mm apart and on living chamber about 20 mm distant. Rather coarse longitudinal striae of two sizes seen in a few places.

Each suture occupies concave interspace between annuli. Septa evenly concave, and depth of curvature approximately equal to length of one camera. Specimen probably mature because two uppermost sutures about 4 mm apart, occurring in interspace.

Siphuncle, cyrtochoanitic, preserved at adapical end of specimen; appears subcentral. Center of siphuncle 22 mm from ventral conch wall and 29 mm from dorsal where dorsoventral conch diameter 51 mm. Its diameter at passage through septum 3 mm. Between septa enlarges to 8 mm. Each segment of siphuncle nearly vase-shaped; connecting ring represents base and septal necks flaring outer lip.

DISCUSSION: *Gorbyoceras giganteum* is distinguished from all previously described species of this genus known to the writer by its large size. Except for this difference it is similar in many respects to one of the types of *Spyroceras (Gorbyoceras) geronticum*, described and illustrated by Foerste and Savage (1927, p. 38, Pl. 6, figs. 1A, B) from the Shamattawa Formation of Gods River, northern Manitoba. Both have sloping annuli on the living chamber. Those of *G. geronticum*, however, slope from ventral to dorsal side, and not from lateral to lateral as do those on *G. giganteum*.

Genus *Ephippiorthoceras* Foerste, 1924

Type Species: *Orthoceras formosum* Billings, 1857

Ephippiorthoceras dowlingi Foerste and Savage

1927 *Ephippiorthoceras dowlingi* FOERSTE and SAVAGE, Denison Univ. Bull., Jour. Sci. Lab., v. 22, p. 43, Pl. 4, figs. 3A, B
1928 [?] *Ephippiorthoceras* sp. (A) FOERSTE, Contr. Mus. Pal., Univ. Michigan, v. 3, no. 3, p. 40, Pl. 3, fig. 3; Pl. 10, fig. 7
1928 [?] *Ephippiorthoceras* sp. (B) FOERSTE, Contr. Mus. Pal., Univ. Michigan, v. 3, no. 3, p. 41, Pl. 4, fig. 4; Pl. 10, fig. 8
1941 [?] *Ephippiorthoceras* sp. I ROY, Field Mus. Nat. Hist. Geol. Mem., v. 2, p. 179 figs. 96a–c
1954 *Ephippiorthoceras dowlingi* Foerste and Savage. MILLER, YOUNGQUIST, AND COLLINSON, Geol. Soc. America Mem. 62, p. 54, Pl. 20, figs. 1–3; Pl. 21, figs. 7, 8; Pl. 22, figs. 2–4; Pl. 44, figs. 13–16; Pl. 51, figs. 1, 2; Pl. 56, figs. 5, 6

OCCURRENCE: One specimen from Member No. 1 of Caution Creek Formation, Churchill River: locality 25280

DESCRIPTION: Species represented by internal mold of phragmocone about 73 mm long in which 14 camerae preserved. Sutures uniformly spaced 5–6 mm apart and form lateral lobes and dorsal and ventral saddles.

DISCUSSION: The primary types are from the Shamattawa Formation of Gods River, northern Manitoba. Miller, Youngquist, and Collinson (1954, p. 54–55) have given a detailed discussion of this species and a fairly long synonymy. *Ephippiorthoceras dowlingi*, apparently, is found in strata other than that equivalent to the Shamattawa Formation for it occurs in the Bighorn Formation of Wyoming (Foerste, 1935) and in the Ordovician of Silliman's Fossil Mount, Baffin Island. Miller, Youngquist, and Collinson pointed out that *E. modestum* Troedsson from the Cape Calhoun Series of northern Greenland and *E. whitewoodense* Miller and Furnish from the Whitewood Formation of South Dakota may be conspecific with this species.

Family CLINOCERATIDAE Flower

Genus *Whiteavesites* Foerste, 1929

Type Species: *Orthoceras Winnipegense* Whiteaves, 1892

"Conch slightly curved lengthwise, with the ventral outline convex. The living chamber contracts upward along its lower half, and then remains of about the same diameter as far as the aperture.

The sutures of the septa curve strongly downward laterally, forming broad dorsal and ventral saddles. The septa are strongly concave dorso-ventrally, but only moderately concave laterally. The siphuncle is located a short distance ventrad of the centre of the conch. The segments of the siphuncle are elongated vertically in a narrowly elliptical manner." (Foerste, 1929, p. 167)

Whiteavesites winnipegensis (Whiteaves)

(Pl. 22, fig. 2)

1892 *Orthoceras Winnipegense* WHITEAVES, Trans. Roy. Soc. Canada, v. 9, sec. 4, p. 82, Pl. 8, figs. 4, 4a, 4b
1897 *Orthoceras Winnipegense* Whiteaves. WHITEAVES, Geol. Surv. Canada Pal. Foss., v. 3, pt. 3, p. 212
1915 *Orthoceras winnipegense* Whiteaves. BASSLER, United States Nat. Mus. Bull. 92, v. 2, p. 919
1929 *Whiteavesites winnipegensis* (Whiteaves). FOERSTE, Denison Univ. Bull., Jour. Sci. Lab., v. 24, p. 167, Pl 2; Pl. 13, fig. 3; Pl. 14, figs. 1A, B

OCCURRENCE: Two specimens from Member No. 2 of Portage Chute Formation. Hypotype (G.S.C. No. 10530) is from South Knife River: locality unknown; the other from Churchill River: locality 25275.

DESCRIPTION: South Knife River specimen best preserved; internal mold approximately 110 mm in length, of which 72 mm belongs to living chamber and remainder to phragmocone.

Specimen has been somewhat obliquely compressed, and since siphuncle not preserved cannot distinguish ventral from dorsal side. Following measurements of conch diameters estimated because of this distortion. Approximately eight camerae present. At lowest, dorsoventral and lateral diameters 30 mm and 40 mm, respectively. Corresponding measurements 28 mm and 36 mm at base of living chamber. Chamber contracts rather abruptly upward to position about 25 mm above its base where dorsoventral and lateral diameters 21 mm and 28 mm, respectively. Little contraction above here, and at uppermost preserved part of living chamber corresponding diameters 17 mm and 28 mm.

Although specimen has been distorted, broad ventral and dorsal saddles and narrower more highly curved lateral lobes present. Adorally, sutures gradually become more closely spaced: at bottom of phragmocone about 6 mm apart and 4 mm orad. As most orad camera has sutures about 1 mm apart, specimen was evidently mature.

DISCUSSION: The primary type of *W. winnipegensis* is from the Dog Head Member of the Red River Formation, southern Manitoba.

Whiteavesites procteri sp. nov.

(Pl. 22, fig. 1; Pl. 30, fig. 2)

OCCURRENCE: One specimen (holotype, G.S.C. No. 10538) from Lower Member of Surprise Creek Formation' Nelson River: locality 25264

DESCRIPTION: Description of species based on holotype, internal mold approximately 110 mm in length of which 57 mm belongs to living chamber and remainder to phragmocone. Only five camerae preserved.

Specimen depressed dorsoventrally so that transverse outline subelliptical and dorsal side more convex than ventral. Lateral sides rather strongly curved, maximum convexity occurring closer to ventral than to dorsal side. In longitudinal outline, lateral sides diverge very gradually orad as far as lower half of living chamber where they contract slightly toward aperture. Dorsal and ventral sides approximately parallel over conch length. Dorsoventral and lateral diameters 33 mm and 42 mm, respectively, at 3 camerae below base of living chamber. Corresponding measurements of this base, an adoral distance of about 30 mm, 35 mm and 50 mm, and at aperture 35 mm and 43 mm, respectively.

Sutures form broad ventral and dorsal saddles, rather sharp lateral lobes, and are uniformly spaced between 8 and 10 mm over phragmocone surface. Difference in height between tops of saddles and bottom of lobes almost equal to depth of one camera. Septa rather deeply concave dorsoventrally, dorsal slope being longer than ventral. Depth of curvature slightly greater than depth of one camera. In lateral profile they are only moderately concave.

Siphuncle poorly preserved so that no details of structure apparent. It appears to have been nearly tubular with perhaps small expansion between septa, between 5 and 7 mm wide, and ventral wall about 4 mm from wall of conch.

DISCUSSION: The species is named in honor of the writer's field assistant: Mr. R. M. Procter.

Order ASCOCERATIDA Flower

Family HEBETOCERATIDAE Flower

Genus *Probillingsites* Foerste, 1928

Type Species: *Probillingsites welleri* Foerste, 1928

"The mature part of the shell, all that is known for any representative of this genus, is a gibbous shell of slightly depressed section consisting of a living chamber and usually not more than four camerae. The septum at the base of the specimen is deeply curved especially vertically, and the deepest part lies ventrad of the centre, where the siphuncle is located. All sutures slope forward from venter to dorsum . . ." (Flower, 1946, p. 192).

Flower (1946), and Miller, Youngquist, and Collinson (1954) have recently discussed this genus in detail. The latter authors described a new species, *Probillingsites belli*, from Silliman's Fossil Mount in southern Baffin Island. One of their paratypes has a preserved siphuncle, the first found in representatives of this genus. They stated (p. 109) that it ". . .consists of short recurved septal necks and connecting rings that are only slightly expanded within the camerae. . ."

Most Trenton species of *Probillingsites* are characterized by having nearly parallel sutures, with adoral ones not oblique to the more adapical sutures. Richmondian species, on the other hand, have markedly more inclined adoral than adapical sutures. The new species, *P. harkeri*, described below, has Richmondian-type sutures.

Probillingsites harkeri sp. nov.

(Pl. 20, figs. 2a, b)

OCCURRENCE: One specimen (holotype, G.S.C. No. 10540) from Member No. 1 of Caution Creek Formation, Churchill River: locality 25281

DESCRIPTION: Holotype internal mold of living chamber, and phragmocone above septum of truncation. Ventral side of living chamber partially destroyed; its probable original outline indicated on illustrations. One lateral side of septum of truncation also destroyed.

Specimen about 65 mm long and dorsoventrally depressed so that transverse outline oval and lateral diameter larger. Adapical part of shell gibbous, and adoral portion produced. Conch expands from blunt apex to estimated dorsoventral and lateral diameters of 27 mm and 32 mm, respectively, measured in horizontal plane passing through ventral part of suture of truncation, a longitudinal distance of about 10 mm above apex. Conch has maximum diameters another 12 mm higher in horizontal plane passing through dorsal part of second suture from base and intersecting ventral side of living chamber approximately 8 mm above ventral part of uppermost suture. Dorsoventral and lateral diameters here 35 mm and 42 mm, respectively. Adorally from this plane, lateral sides of living chamber contract gradually. Dorsal side nearly straight, flares outward slightly in uppermost part, and nearly in line with upper part of phragmocone. Ventral side contracts rapidly and approaches dorsal surface so that aperture, if preserved, would be laterally elongated and have estimated dorsoventral and lateral diameters of 20 mm and 39 mm, respectively.

Septum of truncation nearly horizontal at apex. Ventral surface slopes steeply upward, dorsal more gently inclined. Reconstructed lateral profile nearly semicircular. Ventral part of oblique suture of septum of truncation about 11 mm above apex, measured longitudinally, and dorsal about 27 mm above it. Next three adoral sutures slightly converging ventrally and dip downward from dorsal to ventral side at horizontal angle of about 20°. They are about 4 mm apart on former side and 2 mm on latter. Most orad suture about 4 mm above lower one on dorsal side and slopes rapidly down toward latter on dorsoventral surface and is so close to it on lateral and ventral sides that the two are almost indistinguishable. Traces of adoral septa preserved; they are very gently concave in dorsoventral section in which dorsal part slopes downward at vertical angle of 40° to conch axis. Septa become nearly horizontal near ventral side.

Opening for siphuncle on septum of truncation about halfway between dorsal and ventral side, and closer to one lateral side than to other. Latter position probably caused by postburial deformation. Siphuncle very poorly preserved, and no details of structure apparent. It appears to have been approximately tubular and has diameter of 2–3 mm. Adoral curve almost parallels ventral wall of phragmocone. It is 7–8 mm from this wall.

DISCUSSION: *Probillingsites harkeri* is larger than most of the previously described forms known to the writer. In general outline it is most similar to *P. lebanonensis* Flower from the Arnheim Formation of the Richmond Group, Kentucky but is distinguished from it by its larger size.

The species is named in honor of Dr. Peter Harker of the Geological Survey of Canada.

Family ASCOCERATIDAE Barrande

Genus *Billingsites* Hyatt, 1884

Type Species: *Ascoceras canadense* Billings, 1857

Billingsites costulatus (Whiteaves)

(Pl. 37, fig. 2)

1896 *Ascoceras costulatum* WHITEAVES, Canadian Rec. Sci., v. 6, p. 394
1897 *Ascoceras costulatum* Whiteaves. WHITEAVES, Geol. Surv. Canada Pal. Foss., v. 3, pt. 3, p. 215, Pl. 22, fig. 1
1915 *Ascoceras costulatum* Whiteaves. BASSLER, United States Nat. Mus. Bull. 92, v. 1, p. 79
1929 *Billingsites costulatum* (Whiteaves). FOERSTE, Denison Univ. Bull., Jour. Sci. Lab., v. 24, p. 257, Pl. 13, figs. 1A, B, C

OCCURRENCE: Two specimens from Member No. 2 of Portage Chute Formation. One (hypotype, G.S.C. No. 10527) is from Churchill River: locality 25272; the other from Nelson River: locality 25256

DESCRIPTION: Churchill River specimen more complete and not so depressed dorsoventrally as type specimen. Conch about 90 mm long and maximum dorsoventral and lateral diameters of 44 mm and 50 mm, respectively, at position about 53 mm above base. Dorsal side more convex than ventral and rather humped where diameter greatest. Conch gradually contracts orad to neck, about 75 mm above base, where dorsoventral and lateral diameters 35 mm and 39 mm, respectively. Neck about 10 mm long. Aperture subelliptical in transverse outline. Part of dorsal surface of conch shows well-defined costellae characteristic of species.

Three sutures present and show same pattern and spacing as those on type specimen illustrated by Foerste (1929, Pl. 13, fig. 1C).

Nelson River specimen less complete and more poorly preserved than hypotype. However, some costellae can be seen and conch dimensions approximate those of hypotype.

DISCUSSION: The holotype of *B. costulatus* is from the Dog Head Member of the Red River Formation, southern Manitoba.

Billingsites landerensis Foerste

(Pl. 23, figs. 1a, b)

1935 *Billingsites landerense* FOERSTE, Denison Univ. Bull., Jour. Sci. Lab., v. 30, p. 20, Pl. 1, figs. 4, 5

OCCURRENCE: Two specimens (hypotypes, G.S.C. No. 10799, 10800) from Member No. 2 of Portage Chute Formation, Churchill River: locality 25275

DESCRIPTION: Two specimens referred to this species internal molds. Hypotype No. 10799 best preserved. It has been somewhat obliquely dorsoventrally compressed so that lateral outline proportionally wider than that of holotype. Four sutures present and almost identical in spacing and pattern with those of latter specimen. Uppermost suture not visible on dorsal view shown on Plate 23 because it forms outline of specimen.

Hypotype No. 10800 has escaped compression but is incomplete adorally. Portion preserved, however, nearly identical in size and shape with holotype. Only traces of sutures preserved.

DISCUSSION: The holotype of B. *landerense* is from the Lander Sandstone Member of the Bighorn Formation, Wyoming.

Billingsites borealis (Parks)

(Pl. 22, figs. 4a, b)

1913 *Ascoceras boreale* PARKS (*in* Tyrrell), Bur. Mines Ontario, 22nd Rept., p. 192
1915 *Ascoceras boreale* Parks. BASSLER, United States Nat. Mus. Bull. 92, v. 1, p. 79
1915 *Ascoceras boreale* Parks. PARKS, Trans. Roy. Canadian Inst., v. 11, p. 32, Pl. 2, figs. 8, 9
1927 *Billingsites boreale* (Parks) [*partim*]. FOERSTE and SAVAGE, Denison Univ. Bull., Jour. Sci. Lab., v. 22, p. 30, Pl. 3, figs. 2, 4A-D

OCCURRENCE: Two specimens from Member No. 1 of Caution Creek Formation, Churchill River: localities 25280, 25282; and two from Upper Member of this formation, South Knife River: locality 25304

Hypotype, G.S.C. No. 10528: Member No. 1, Caution Creek Formation, Churchill River, locality 25282

Hypotype, G.S.C. No. 10529: Member No. 1, Caution Creek Formation, Churchill River, locality 25280

DISCUSSION: *Billingsites borealis* differs from B. *keatingi* in being larger and dorsoventrally depressed. For further remarks on this species, see the discussion of B. *keatingi*.

Billingsites keatingi sp. nov.

(Pl. 22, figs. 3a, b)

1927 *Billingsites boreale* FOERSTE and SAVAGE [*partim*], Denison Univ. Bull., Jour. Sci. Lab., v. 22, p. 30, Pl. 3, figs. 3A, B

OCCURRENCE: One specimen (holotype, G.S.C. No. 10558) from Member No. 1 of Caution Creek Formation, Churchill River: locality 25280

DESCRIPTION: Conch ovoid, about 30 mm long, and only slightly depressed dorsoventrally, with subcircular transverse outline. In dorsoventral profile lower end narrowly rounded, and sides gradually diverge upward to level of third suture and then converge slightly. Base broadly rounded in lateral profile, almost semicircular; sides diverge upward more rapidly than dorsal and ventral surfaces and converge slightly above level of third suture. About 8 mm above base, at level of suture coalescence, dorsoventral and lateral diameters 14 mm and 17.5 mm, respectively. At level of third suture, 27 mm above base, corresponding measurements 18 mm and 21.5 mm. Conch walls contract inward above this point to uppermost part of shell, at level of fourth suture. Dorsoventral and lateral diameters at this suture 16 mm and 21 mm, respectively.

Dorsal surface of upper third of conch crossed by four transverse sutures which bend strongly apicad along ventrolateral sides and then curve gently downward and toward dorsal side, gradually approach one another until they coalesce at points about 13.5 mm apart, measured across dorsal surface, and 8 mm above base. Suture of coalescence curves downward from here and across ventral side as shallow lobe. Its angle with horizontal about 25° in dorsoventral profile.

DISCUSSION: Foerste and Savage (1927) described and illustrated the "type" specimen of B. *borealis* (Parks) and two other specimens which they referred to this species. All are from the Shamattawa Formation of Gods River, northern Manitoba. The type and one of the specimens (No. 5 HB in the Savage collection) are both dorsoventrally depressed. The third specimen (No. 6 HB in the Savage collection), however, was commented upon by these authors because of its small size and nearly circular transverse outline. The present writer has found the latter type of *Billingsites*, as well as typically dorsoventrally depressed specimens of *B. borealis* in the Caution Creek Formation, and considers that they represent a new species, here called *Billingsites keatingi* in honor of his field assistant, Mr. L. M. Keating.

Billingsites canadensis (Billings)(?)

1857 *Ascoceras Canadense* BILLINGS, Geol. Surv. Canada Rept. Prog., 1853–1856, p. 310
1863 *Ascoceras Canadense* Billings. BILLINGS, Geol. Surv. Canada, Geol. Canada, p. 218, fig. 227
1884 *Billingsites canadense* (Billings). HYATT, Proc. Boston Soc. Nat. Hist., v. 22, p. 278
1889 *Ascoceras Canadense* Billings. MILLER, North American Geol. Pal., p. 432, fig. 726
1915 *Billingsites canadensis* (Billings). BASSLER, United States Nat. Mus. Bull. 92, v. 1, p. 125
1928 *Billingsites canadensis* (Billings). FOERSTE (*in* Twenhofel), Geol. Surv. Canada Mem. 154, p. 260, Pl. 40, fig. 3
1952 *Billingsites canadensis* (Billings). MOORE, LALICKER, and FISCHER, Invertebrate Foss., p. 357, fig. 5

OCCURRENCE: One specimen from Member No. 1 of Caution Creek Formation, Churchill River: locality 25277

DISCUSSION: The Churchill River specimen is fragmentary and consists only of the adapical part of the conch. In its size and shape, as well as the angle of coalescence of sutures it is very similar to *B. canadensis*. The writer prefers to refer it questionably to this species, however, because of its fragmentary nature.

Billingsites canadensis occurs in the English Head and Vaureal formations on Anticosti Island.

Order ONCOCERATIDA Flower, *in* Flower and Kummel

Family ONCOCERATIDAE Hyatt

Genus *Digenuoceras* Foerste, 1935

Type Species: *Oxygonioceras*(?) *latum* Foerste, 1929

"This genotype [*Oxygonioceras*(?) *latum*] differs from typical *Oxygonioceras* in its cross section, both the dorsal, as well as the ventral outline of the cross section being acutely angular. The segments of the siphuncle are subfusiform. . . . " (Foerste, 1935, p. 43–44).

Flower (1946, p. 229, 303) has discussed the affinities of *Digenuoceras* in detail.

Digenuoceras latum (Foerste)

(Pl. 23, fig. 3)

1929 *Oxygonioceras*(?) *latum* FOERSTE, Denison Univ. Bull., Jour. Sci. Lab., v. 24, p. 218, Pl. 18, figs. 1, 2; Pl. 19, fig. 2
1935 *Digenuoceras latum* (Foerste). FOERSTE, Denison Univ. Bull., Jour. Sci. Lab., v. 30, p. 43
1935 [?] *Digenuoceras* cf. *latum* (Foerste). FOERSTE, Denison Univ. Bull., Jour. Sci. Lab., v. 30, p. 44, Pl. 19, fig. 5
1957 *Digenuoceras latum* (Foerste). SWEET and MILLER, Geol. Surv. Canada Bull. 38, p. 47, Pl. 7, fig. 3; Pl. 8, fig. 1

OCCURRENCE: Two specimens from Member No. 2 of Portage Chute Formation. One (hypotype, G.S.C. No. 10551) is from Churchill River: locality 25276; and the other from South Knife River: locality 25299

DESCRIPTION: Both specimens internal molds of phragmocones. Churchill River specimen more complete, about 245 mm long, measured along median-lateral sides, and contains about 43 camerae. Specimen curved lengthwise, but since much of dorsal and ventral margins incomplete, impossible to give accurate radii of curvature for them. At 23 camerae, or 160 mm below top of specimen, dorsoventral and lateral diameters 55 mm (estimated) and 22 mm, respectively. Corresponding dimensions 80 mm and 32 mm at top of phragmocone. Both dorsal and ventral margins angulated in lower part of phragmocone. Adorally, however, dorsal margin becomes narrowly rounded.

Sutures form broad shallow lateral lobes and acute dorsal and ventral saddles. Bottoms of lobes about 1½ camerae below tops of corresponding saddles. Apicad sutures between 3½ to 4 mm apart along median-lateral sides. Adorally they become more distant and are 6–7 mm apart on upper part of phragmocone. Septa have very little lateral concavity but strongly curved dorsoventrally.

South Knife River specimen sectioned longitudinally in dorsoventral plane. Siphuncle lies near ventral wall and has average diameter of about 5 mm between septa, where corresponding dorsoventral conch diameter 60 mm. Connecting rings nearly tubular and almost parallel ventral conch wall but constricted abruptly where they come in contact with septa. General appearance of siphuncle similar to that of Portage Chute specimen (G.S.C. hypotype No. 10554) of *Exomegoceras wyomingense* Miller and Carrier.

DISCUSSION: The primary types of *D. latum* are from the Dog Head Member of the Red River Formation, southern Manitoba. Foerste (1935, p. 44) has also compared a specimen from the "basal part" of the Bighorn Formation, Wyoming, to this species. It is questionably included in synonymy.

Digenuoceras mclearni sp. nov.

(Pl. 21, fig. 1)

OCCURRENCE: One specimen (holotype, G.S.C. No. 10345) from Member No. 1 of Caution Creek Formation, Churchill River: locality 25278

DESCRIPTION: Holotype well-preserved internal mold, curved lengthwise; concave dorsal side has radius of curvature of about 95 mm and convex ventral side 130 mm. Maximum length of preserved portion of living chamber approximately 75 mm, measured along median-lateral sides, and that of phragmocone 86 mm. Latter has 14 camerae preserved.

Dorsal and ventral walls of conch gradually diverge orad, but lateral sides diverge only slightly. At preserved base of phragmocone dorsoventral and lateral diameters 89 mm and 31 mm, respectively. Corresponding measurements 108 mm and 34 mm (estimated) at base of living chamber. Ventral wall of living chamber incomplete so not possible to give dimensions for more orad parts. Curvature of both dorsal and ventral sides of this chamber, however, appears to be same as that of corresponding adapical sides of phragmocone. Thus, chamber probably expands gradually orad at about same rate as phragmocone. Dorsal and ventral sides of phragmocone and lower part of living chamber sharply acute in transverse outline. Toward upper part of chamber, however, dorsal wall gradually becomes rounded.

Sutures cross lateral sides as broad shallow lobes and form acute dorsal and ventral saddles. Bottoms of lobes about 2½ camerae or 15 mm below tops of corresponding saddles. Adorally sutures rise progressively higher from ventral to dorsal side so that uppermost ventral saddle about 27 mm higher than corresponding dorsal one. Sutures about 3 mm apart along dorsal wall; 6–7 mm along middle of lateral sides; and about 9 mm along ventral wall. Septa concave dorsoventrally but appear to have little lateral curvature.

DISCUSSION: The species is named in honor of Dr. F. H. McLearn, formerly of the Geological Survey of Canada.

From *Digenuoceras latum* (Foerste), *D. mclearni* differs in its larger size and wider conch. *Digenuoceras okulitchi* sp. nov. has the ventral side much more acute than the dorsal.

Digenuoceras okulitchi sp. nov.

(Pl. 25, fig. 2; Pl. 30, fig. 1)

OCCURRENCE: Four specimens from Chasm Creek Formation. Two are from Member No. 2: locality 25285; and one from Member No. 3: locality 25290, Churchill River. The fourth is from Nelson River: locality 25269

Holotype, G.S.C. No. 10510: Member No. 2, Chasm Creek Formation, Churchill River, locality 25285
Paratype, G.S.C. No. 10511: Member No. 3, Chasm Creek Formation, Churchill River, locality 25290

DESCRIPTION: Holotype best preserved and most complete specimen collected; internal mold about 300 mm in length, measured along median-lateral sides, of which about 70 mm belongs to living chamber and remainder to phragmocone. An estimated 30–32 camerae preserved in latter. Ventral side broken off at several places Specimen curved lengthwise and radius of curvature for concave dorsal side about 105 mm. Ventral outline approximately concentric with dorsal. Specimen strongly depressed laterally. Both dorsal and ventral margins acute, latter much more so than former. Maximum lateral diameter, at any one position, in most specimens occurs about a third of the transverse distance from dorsal to ventral side. In longitudinal outline conch shows little orad increase in diameter either dorsoventrally or laterally. Near preserved base of phragmocone, about 28 camerae or 200 mm below living chamber dorsoventral and lateral diameters 110 mm (estimated) and 40 mm, respectively. At about 65 mm or 8 camerae apicad of this chamber corresponding dimensions 115 mm and 42 mm; and at base of this chamber 122 mm (estimated) and 48 mm. From here to aperture dorsoventral diameter changes very little. Lateral sides, however, show slight constriction about 40 mm above base, but this may be caused by postburial compaction.

Sutures form lateral lobes and acute dorsal and ventral saddles. Bottoms of apicad lobes about 4 camerae or 34 mm below tops of corresponding saddles. Near top of phragmocone curvature gradually decreases so that bottoms about 2 camerae or 20 mm below saddles. Apicad sutures about 2–3 mm apart on dorsal, 6–7 mm on median-lateral and about 8–9 mm (estimated) on ventral side. Adorally they gradually become more distant and rise progressively higher from dorsal to ventral side. They are about 4 mm apart on dorsal, 10 mm on median-lateral, and about 14 mm (estimated) on ventral side near living chamber.

Paratype is portion of phragmocone about 170 mm long, to which some altered shell material adheres. On lateral and ventral surfaces material between 1 and 3 mm thick. It thickens to about 7 mm along dorsal margin, however, and outer surface rather sharply acute, much more so than underlying internal mold of dorsal wall. In life, therefore, both dorsal and ventral walls of animal were acute.

DISCUSSION: *Digenuoceras okulitchi* differs from *D. latum* (Foerste) in its larger size and less acute dorsal margins. It is most closely related to *D. mclearni* sp. nov. Dorsal and ventral margins of the latter species, however, are equally acute, whereas the ventral margin of *D. okulitchi* is much more acute, on the internal mold, than the dorsal.

The species is named in honor of Professor V. J. Okulitch of the University of British Columbia.

Genus *Exomegoceras* Miller and Carrier, 1942

Type Species: *Exomegoceras wyomingense* Miller and Carrier, 1942

The genus *Exomegoceras* contains exogastrically curved nautiloids with a strongly compressed conch. The narrowly to broadly rounded dorsal side and the acutely angular ventral side, produce a roughly tear-drop-shaped transverse outline.

Sutures form broadly rounded lateral lobes, rounded dorsal saddles, and acutely angular ventral saddles.

Siphuncular structures are apparently poorly preserved in the primary types of *Exomegoceras wyomingense*. Miller and Carrier (1942) thought that the siphuncle was ventral, and that its segments were slightly expanded between septa. A fairly well-preserved Churchill River specimen referred to *E. wyomingense* shows the siphuncle to be rather similar in structure and outline to those occurring in representatives of *Winnipegoceras* and *Westonoceras*: i.e., it is approximately tubular and contracts abruptly near the passage through a septum.

Miller and Carrier considered *Exomegoceras* to differ from the genus *Digenuoceras* Foerste in having the dorsal side rounded rather than angular. The present writer thinks that these two may prove to be congeneric. The type specimen of *D. latum* is probably more strongly laterally compressed than is normal for the species. A Churchill River specimen referred to *D. latum* has a proportionally greater lateral to dorso ventral diameter than the holotype, and adorally the dorsal side becomes rounded as in *Exomegoceras*.

Exomegoceras wyomingense Miller and Carrier

(Pl. 31, fig. 1)

1942 *Exomegoceras wyomingense* MILLER and CARRIER, Jour. Pal., v. 16, no. 5, p. 541, Pl. 76, figs. 1–4; fig. 2

OCCURRENCE: One specimen (hypotype, G.S.C. No. 10554) from Member No. 2 of the Portage Chute Formation, Churchill River: locality 25272

DESCRIPTION: Churchill River specimen considerably more complete than primary types. Phragmocone about 97 mm long, measured along median-lateral sides, and contains 12 camerae. Living chamber 56 mm long. Radius of curvature of ventral side 115 mm. That of dorsal side shorter: about 90 mm. Specimen gradually expands orad, and there does not appear to be any contraction of living chamber as mentioned by Miller and Carrier (1942, p. 541) in diagnosis of genus. At preserved base of specimen dorsoventral diameter 45 mm and lateral diameter 20 mm. Corresponding measurements 60 mm and 35 mm at base of living chamber. At top of this chamber 61 mm and 39 mm, respectively.

Sutures have nearly same pattern and spacing as primary types.

Siphuncle fairly well preserved in hypotype. It lies very close to ventral wall, and maximum diameter about 7 mm. Connecting rings tubular, almost parallel to walls of conch, but contract abruptly where they come in contact with septa.

DISCUSSION: *Exomegoceras wyomingense* was originally described from the dolomite member of the Bighorn Formation, Wyoming.

Genus *Neumatoceras* Foerste, 1935

Neumatoceras churchillense sp. nov.

(Pl. 36, figs. 2 a, b)

OCCURRENCE: One specimen (holotype, G.S.C. No. 10559) from Member No. 2 of Portage Chute Formation, Churchill River: locality 25272

DESCRIPTION: Specimen referred to this species well preserved internal mold about 61 mm in length, measured along median-lateral sides, of which 34 mm belongs to phragmocone and remainder to living chamber. Former retains nine camerae.

Ventral wall uniformly convex with radius of curvature approximately 47 mm in longitudinal outline. Dorsal wall of phragmocone nearly straight, but that of living chamber curved rather abruptly and has radius of curvature about 27 mm. In transverse section outline subelliptical; dorsal side broadly rounded and ventral very narrowly rounded, almost angular. Dorsoventral diameter 24 mm and lateral 17 mm at preserved base of phragmocone. Five camerae below living chamber where conch widest, corresponding measurements 30 mm and 26 mm (estimated), and at base of this chamber 28 mm and 22 mm (estimated), respectively. Living chamber gradually contracts orad and at aperture dorsoventral and lateral diameters 25 mm and 12 mm, respectively.

Sutures 3 mm apart on dorsal, 4 mm on lateral, and 5 mm apart on ventral side. Nearly transverse on lower part of phragmocone and bend slightly upward toward ventral side. Adorally they rise progressively from dorsal to ventral walls so that uppermost suture has horizontal angle of about 20°.

DISCUSSION: *Neumatoceras churchillense* is similar in pattern and spacing of sutures to the Fremont specimen of *Neumatoceras* sp. described by Foerste (1935, p. 38). On the latter, however, dorsal and ventral walls of living chamber are not as strongly curved lengthwise as on the Churchill River specimen. *Neumatoceras churchillense* is also very similar to *N. gibberosum* Foerste (1935, p. 32) from the Bighorn Formation of Wyoming, but it is not so gibbous along the ventral wall. Foerste (*in* Twenhofel, 1928, p. 305-306) described a specimen from the Ellis Bay Formation of Anticosti Island which he called *Beloitoceras percurvatum*. This species should be placed in *Neumatoceras* because the maximum dorsoventral diameter of the conch is below the base of the living chamber. *Neumatoceras churchillense* is very similar to this species in its size, outline, and the pattern and spacing of sutures but differs in that the dorsal side of the phragmocone is not curved.

Order DISCOSORIDA Flower

Family WESTONOCERATIDAE Teichert

Genus *Westonoceras* Foerste, 1926

Type Species: *Cyrtoceras Manitobense* Whiteaves, 1890

Following Flower (1946, p. 438-441), Miller, Youngquist, and Collinson's (1954, p. 84) diagnosis of this genus is as follows:

"Conch cyrtoceraconic (being curved exogastrically) but during adolescence may be essentially straight. Cross section typically compressed and varies from subcircular to elliptical or oval, with venter commonly more narrowly rounded than dorsum. At full maturity, adoral portion of phragmocone strongly convex ventrally and slightly so dorsally, and body chamber contracted orad. Typically sutures are almost straight during adolescence but form prominent ventral saddles at maturity. Siphuncle fairly close to ventral wall of conch and cyrtochoanitic in structure, being composed of thickly subdiscoidal segments that are subquadrate in longitudinal section. Septal necks short and so strongly recurved that they are recumbent, and connecting rings are in contact with septa both adorally and adapically."

Westonoceras differs from *Winnipegoceras* in that the conch is not markedly curved lengthwise. Miller, Youngquist and Collinson, (p. 85) have suggested that *Neumatoceras* should probably be regarded as a synonym for *Westonoceras*, but Flower (*in* Flower and Teichert, 1957, p. 71) has disputed this assignment.

Westonoceras nelsonense Foerste

1929 *Westonoceras nelsonense* FOERSTE, Denison Univ. Bull., Jour. Sci. Lab., v. 24, p. 223, Pl. 38, fig. 1
1957 *Westonoceras nelsonense* Foerste. FLOWER (*in* Flower and Teichert), Univ. Kansas, Pal. Contr. mollusca, art. 6, p. 72

OCCURRENCE: Six specimens from Member No. 2 of Portage Chute Formation. Two are from Nelson River: localities 25254, 25257; two from Churchill River: locality 25275; and two from South Knife River: localities 25297, 25300

Hypotype, G.S.C. No. 10509: Member No. 2, Portage Chute Formation, South Knife River, locality 25300

DESCRIPTION: Type specimen of *W. nelsonense* from Member No. 2 of Portage Chute Formation (Nelson River Formation of Savage and Van Tuyl) on Nelson River and probably collected from locality 25258. It has been compressed somewhat obliquely in dorsoventral direction, and most specimens collected by present writer also have such distortion. Hypotype No. 10509, however, appears to have escaped distortion and although larger than type, has approximately same shape so it is referred to *W. nelsonense*. Conch approximately 170 mm in length, of which about 50 mm belongs to living chamber and remainder to phragmocone. At lowest preserved part of phragmocone, 17 camerae below living chamber, dorsoventral and lateral diameters 37 mm and 32 mm, respectively. Phragmocone slowly enlarges orad to maximum dorsoventral and lateral diameters of 74 mm and 64 mm (estimated), respectively, at about 6 camerae below living chamber. Corresponding dimensions 61 mm and 55 mm (estimated) at base of this chamber. About 30 mm above base they are 49 mm and 40 mm (estimated), respectively. In transverse section outline subelliptical, and dorsoventral diameter is larger. Dorsal side rounded, whereas ventral nearly subangular.

Sutures about 8 mm apart in lower part of phragmocone and gradually become closer, until about 6 mm apart near living chamber. Specimen evidently mature because uppermost camera has sutures about 3 mm apart. Sutures slope downward from dorsal to ventral side and form shallow lateral lobes, weak dorsal saddles, and curve upward to form rounded ventral saddles in lower part of phragmocone. Adorally dorsal to ventral slope decreases and at position of maximum conch diameter, six camerae below living chamber, sutures nearly transverse. Above here they slope upward from dorsal to ventral side and form small rounded ventral saddles.

Genus *Winnipegoceras* Foerste, 1928

Type Species: *Cyrtoceras laticurvatum* Whiteaves, 1896

The conch is curved lengthwise; the ventral side is convex and the dorsal concave. The phragmocone expands gradually orad and the greatest diameters are 4–10 camerae below the base of the living chamber where the ventral side is weakly humped. Adorally it contracts gradually and the living chamber may be relatively long and attenuated or contracted rather rapidly so that the aperture is somewhat constricted. In transverse section the outline is elliptical, and the dorsoventral diameter is the larger.

Sutures form broad shallow lateral lobes and dorsal and ventral saddles.

The siphuncle is near the ventral wall, and its structure is poorly understood. It expands considerably between septa and is tubular or quadrangular in outline. Siphuncles of the first three species of *Winnipegoceras*, described below, were sectioned in a dorsoventral plane. The dorsal part of the septal neck is thought to be recurved back onto the septum for a short distance and then to make a right-angle bend to join the dorsal part of the connecting ring. The latter is nearly straight for most of its length, and the lower part is curved strongly inward to the area of adnation. The ventral part of the neck appears to be bent sharply and almost at right angles to the septum and continues without marked change in curvature onto the ring which is gently convex ventrally. The lower part of the ring appears to abut against, and bend sharply onto the septum at the area of adnation.

Winnipegoceras laticurvatum (Whiteaves)

(Pl. 23, fig. 4; Pl. 27, fig. 2)

1896 *Cyrtoceras laticurvatum* WHITEAVES, Canadian Rec. Sci., v. 6, p. 396
1897 *Cyrtoceras laticurvatum* Whiteaves. WHITEAVES, Geol. Surv. Canada Pal. Foss., v. 3, pt. 3, p. 224, fig. 14
1915 *Cyrtoceras laticurvatum* Whiteaves. BASSLER, United States Nat. Mus. Bull. 92, v. 1, p. 353
1928 *Winnipegoceras laticurvatum* (Whiteaves). FOERSTE, Contr. Mus. Pal., Univ. Michigan, v. 3, no. 3, p. 56, Pl. 9, figs. 1, 2
1929 *Winnipegoceras laticurvatum* (Whiteaves). FOERSTE, Denison Univ. Bull., Jour. Sci. Lab., v. 24, p. 216
1935 [?] *Winnipegoceras laticurvatum* (Whiteaves). FOERSTE, Denison Univ. Bull., Jour. Sci. Lab., v. 30, p. 38, Pl. 4, fig. 2
1941 *Winnipegoceras laticurvatum* (Whiteaves). ROY, Field Mus. Nat. Hist. Geol. Mem. v. 2, p. 143, fig. 105
1942 [?] *Winnipegoceras laticurvatum* (Whiteaves). MILLER and CARRIER, Jour. Pal., v. 16, no. 5, p. 540, Pl. 78, fig. 6
1947 [non] *Winnipegoceras laticurvatum* (Whiteaves). MILLER and YOUNGQUIST, Jour. Pal., v. 21, no. 5, p. 415, Pl. 56, fig. 2
1954 [?] *Winnipegoceras* aff. *W. laticurvatum* (Whiteaves). MILLER, YOUNGQUIST, and COLLINSON, Geol. Soc. America Mem. 62, p. 100, Pl. 52, figs. 1–3
1957 *Winnipegoceras laticurvatum* (Whiteaves). FLOWER (*in* Flower and Teichert), Univ. Kansas, Pal. Contr., Mollusca, pt. 6, p. 78, figs. 20A, B

OCCURRENCE: Three specimens from Member No. 2 of Portage Chute Formation. One is from Nelson River: locality 25254; one from Churchill River: locality 25275; and one (hypotype, G.S.C. No. 10548) from South Knife River: locality 25299

DESCRIPTION: South Knife River specimen most complete and best preserved individual found. Living chamber and uppermost 15 camerae nearly complete. Below fifteenth camera are eight partially preserved camerae, with ventral sides missing.

Specimen about 250 mm long, measured along median-lateral sides; 100 mm belongs to living chamber and remainder to phragmocone. As dorsal side of latter strongly curved and ventral less so, conch weakly humped from 9 to 12 camerae below base of living chamber which is nearly straight. In transverse outline it is elliptical and lateral diameter longer. At 14 camerae below living chamber dorsoventral and lateral diameters 46 mm and 28 mm, respectively; 10 camerae below chamber, where phragmocone most strongly humped, diameters 49 mm and 35 mm, respectively. Corresponding measurements 39 mm and 26 mm at base of living chamber. Living chamber very gradually contracts orad to within about 15 mm of aperture. Dorsoventral and lateral dimensions here 34 mm and 20 mm, respectively. There is suggestion of very weak flaring at aperture.

Sutures form broad lateral lobes, and well-defined dorsal and ventral saddles which generally rise to height equal to depth of 1–1½ camerae above corresponding lobes, measured along lateral sides. Sutures have average spacing of 5 mm, 8 mm, and 7 mm, along dorsal, ventral, and lateral surfaces, respectively. Specimen evidently mature as uppermost camera much shorter than others: about 2 mm long on lateral sides. Septa concave both dorsoventrally and laterally, and former curvature stronger than latter. Dorsoventral concavity, measured 14 camerae below living chamber, about equal to depth of 2 camerae, and corresponding lateral concavity about half a camera. Adorally concavity of septa increases until at base of living chamber dorsoventral curvature nearly equivalent to depth of 2½ camerae and lateral about 1½ camerae.

Siphuncle nearly elliptical in transverse outline and dorsoventral axis is longer. Ventral wall 4–5 mm from ventral side of conch, between 7 and 10 camerae below living chamber. At passage through septum, diameter about 4 mm. In longitudinal outline it enlarges between septa to diameter of 6–7 mm and has roughly quadrangular appearance. Siphuncle of South Knife River specimen well-preserved and was sectioned in dorsoventral plane. Although cyrtochoanitic, structure of septal necks not well understood. Necks bend apicad for about 1 mm on ventral side and are gently recurved. Connecting ring continues downward from neck with little change in curvature for about ¼ of length of camera, then straightens for lower ¾ and abuts sharply against lower septum about 1 mm ventrally from upper part of neck of this latter septum. Dorsal septal neck so sharply recurved back on its septum that it is almost indistinguishable from it. Connecting ring leaves this part of neck and is nearly straight for about ¾ of its distance downward toward lower septum, where it curves gently inward to area of adnation. Thus ventral and dorsal curvature of connecting rings are reverse of one another: between septa upper ¼ of ventral part of ring is gently curved and lower ¾ nearly straight, whereas in its dorsal counterpart upper ¾ straight and lower ¼ curved.

DISCUSSION: Although *W. laticurvatum* is apparently nowhere abundant it may have a wide geographic distribution. The primary types are from the Dog Head Member of the Red River Formation, southern Manitoba. Possible representatives have been described by Foerste (1935) from the Lander Sandstone Member of the Bighorn Formation of Wyoming; by Miller and Carrier (1942) from the overlying dolomite member of this formation, and by Miller, Youngquist, and Collinson (1954) from Silliman's Fossil Mount in southern Baffin Island. Miller and Furnish (1937) described and illustrated a specimen from the Matapedia Group of Quebec similar to *W. laticurvatum*.

Winnipegoceras dowlingi Foerste

(Pl. 26, fig. 2; Pl. 31, fig. 4)

1928 *Winnipegoceras dowlingi* FOERSTE, Contr. Mus. Pal., Univ. Michigan, v. 3, no. 3, p. 58, Pl. 8, fig. 1
1929 *Winnipegoceras dowlingi* Foerste. FOERSTE, Denison Univ. Bull., Jour. Sci. Lab., v. 24, p. 217
1954 [?] *Winnipegoceras royi* MILLER, YOUNGQUIST, and COLLINSON, Geol. Soc. America Mem. 62, p. 101, Pl. 32, figs. 1, 2; Pl. 52, figs. 4, 5
1957 [?*non*] *Cyrtogomphoceras dowlingi* (Foerste). FLOWER (*in* Flower and Teichert), Univ. Kansas, Pal. Contr., mollusca, art. 6, p. 62, Pl. 6, figs. 5, 6

Occurrence: Four specimens from Member No. 2 of the Portage Chute Formation. Two are from Nelson River: localities 25254, 25258; and two from South Knife River: localities 25295, 25297

Hypotypes, G.S.C. No. 10549, 10887:   Member No. 2, Portage Chute Formation, Nelson River, localities 25258, 25254, respectively

DESCRIPTION: Northern Manitoban specimens much more complete and better preserved internal molds than type specimen. Hypotype No. 10549 best preserved in collection: approximately 245 mm long, measured along median-lateral sides; about 95 mm belongs to living chamber and remainder to phragmocone. Latter very nearly complete: estimated 40–50 mm of apical end missing. Ventral side uniformly convex and has radius of curvature of about 120 mm in longitudinal outline. Dorsal outline nearly straight along lower part of living chamber and upper eight camerae of phragmocone but gently curved adorally and adapically from here. Transverse outline elliptical, and dorsoventral diameter is larger. At base of lowest preserved septum, about 18 camerae below living chamber, dorsoventral and lateral diameters 22 mm and 17 mm, respectively. Specimen gradually enlarges orad and reaches greatest width about 4 camerae below living chamber, where dorsoventral diameter 74 mm and lateral one 50 mm. Adorally it contracts gradually. Dorsoventral and lateral measurements 54 mm and 29 mm at preserved top of living chamber.

Apicad sutures nearly transverse. Adorally they rise progressively higher from dorsal to ventral side and form weak lateral lobes. Uppermost suture makes horizontal angle of about 30° with conch axis. In lower part of phragmocone sutures spaced about 5 mm, 6 mm, and 8 mm apart on dorsal, lateral, and ventral surfaces, respectively. They become progressively farther apart adorally so that corresponding spacing near living chamber 7 mm, 11 mm, and 15 mm, respectively.

Hypotype No. 10887 almost identical in size and shape with above specimen except that aperture of living chamber more constricted and surface more poorly preserved. It was sectioned longitudinally in dorsoventral plane for details of septa and siphuncle. At lowest preserved portion of phragmocone, an estimated 16–17 camerae below living chamber, septa gently concave both dorsoventrally and laterally and have maximum depth of curvature of about 4 mm, or equivalent of ¾ length of a camera. Adorally they increase in spacing and curvature until near living chamber they have depth of about 17 mm, or equivalent of length of 2 camerae.

Siphuncle in hypotype No. 10887 fairly well preserved. Ventral side about 3 mm from ventral conch wall in lower part of phragmocone and about 5 mm in upper part. Its maximum diameters at these two positions 4 mm and 7 mm, respectively. General appearance of siphuncle very similar to that of type of *Winnipegoceras laticurvatum* (*see* Foerste, 1928, Pl. 9, fig. 1). Nothing regarded with certainty as septal neck seen, although it would appear this structure must be almost at right angles to septum on ventral side, and sharply recurved back onto, and parallel to it on dorsal side. Ventral part of neck presumably extends onto connecting ring without marked change in curvature. Latter gently convex ventrally and abuts sharply against lower septum. Dorsal part of neck probably bends nearly at right angles after leaving position of recurvature, to join connecting ring. Upper three-quarters of dorsal side of ring nearly straight and then curves strongly in to area of adnation.

DISCUSSION: The Nelson and South Knife River specimens have been compared with the type specimen from the Dog Head Member of the Red River Formation, southern Manitoba. Although this specimen is very poorly preserved the writer is certain that his specimens belong to this species. *Winnipegoceras royi*, recently described by Miller, Youngquist, and Collinson (1954) from Silliman's Fossil Mount in southern Baffin Island is very similar to the northern Manitoban *W. dowlingi*. The Baffin Island specimens are fragmentary and consist of the lower part of the living chamber and upper part of the phragmocone. The paratype of *W. royi*, figured on their Plate 52 is almost identical with the Nelson River hypotypes. The holotype of *W. royi*, however, has a similar dorsoventral diameter in relation to the corresponding lateral diameter but proportionally more closely spaced sutures. The writer is of the opinion that *W. royi* may be conspecific with *W. dowlingi* and is accordingly placing it in synonymy.

Flower (*in* Flower and Teichert, 1957, p. 62) stated that *W. dowlingi* is actually a *Cyrtogomphoceras* and based his conclusion on specimens from the type locality which belong to the latter genus. No information is available on the position of siphuncle in the type specimen. Until more is known about its internal structure, the generic position of the type specimen must stand in doubt. If Flower's diagnosis is correct, the northern Manitoban specimens probably belong in *Winnipegoceras royi* Miller, Youngquist, and Collinson.

Winnipegoceras nelsonense sp. nov.
(Pl. 24, fig. 2; Pl. 28, fig. 2; Pl. 32, fig. 3)

OCCURRENCE: One specimen (holotype, G.S.C. No. 10791) from Member No. 2 of Portage Chute Formation, Nelson River: locality 25254

DESCRIPTION: Holotype internal mold of living chamber and 15 camerae with lateral sides somewhat distorted. Its length, measured along ventral side approximately 225 mm, of which 90 mm belongs to living chamber and remainder to phragmocone. Specimen strongly curved exogastrically, and longitudinal ventral outline nearly semi-circular with radius of curvature about 65 mm. Dorsal side less regularly curved: living chamber concave, but profile of uppermost 6–7 camerae nearly straight, and becomes concave below here. This gives specimen slightly humped appearance in dorsoventral outline about four camerae below living chamber. Transverse outline subelliptical, and dorsoventral axis is larger. Both dorsal and ventral margins subacutely rounded. Dorsoventral and lateral diameters 23 mm and 20 mm, respectively, at preserved base of specimen. At four camerae below living chamber where weak humping most pronounced, conch has maximum transverse dimensions of 54 mm dorsoventrally and 42 mm laterally. Corresponding measurements 51 mm and

39 mm at base of living chamber. Walls of living chamber contract rapidly orad particularly in dorsoventral direction. Dimensions of aperture estimated to be 21 mm dorsoventrally and 11 mm laterally.

Sutures nearly transverse but develop very shallow lateral lobes toward upper part of phragmocone. Along dorsal, lateral, and ventral surfaces their average spacing estimated at 3 mm, 8 mm and 11 mm, respectively. Septa concave both dorsoventrally and laterally. Along former direction their curvature approximately equal to depth of little more than two camerae, measured about six camerae below living chamber. Lateral curvature at same position equal to depth of one camera.

Siphuncle, which is very poorly preserved, has been sectioned dorsoventrally through uppermost six camerae. It almost touches ventral wall and has diameter of about 3 mm at passage through septum. Between septa it enlarges to 4 mm. Structure of septal necks and connecting rings almost identical with that of South Knife River specimen (G.S.C. hypotype No. 10548) of *Winnipegoceras laticurvatum*. Only difference in appearance of siphuncle between *W. nelsonense* and *W. laticurvatum* is that in former species septa are, in proportion to maximum diameter of siphuncle, farther apart. This gives siphuncle more oblong appearance than in *W. laticurvatum*.

DISCUSSION: *Winnipegoceras nelsonense* appears most closely related to *W. laticurvatum* (Whiteaves). It differs in its smaller size, larger dorsoventral diameter in proportion to its length, and in having a much less attenuated, almost stubby, living chamber.

Winnipegoceras(?) *contractum* (Foerste and Savage)

1927 *Westenoceras*(?) *contractum* FOERSTE and SAVAGE, Denison Univ. Bull., Jour. Sci. Lab., v. 22, p. 55, Pl. 16, figs. 2A, B
1929 *Winnipegoceras contractum* (Foerste and Savage). FOERSTE, Denison Univ. Bull., Jour. Sci. Lab., v. 24, p. 216
1957 *Neumatoceras? contractum* (Foerste and Savage). FLOWER (*in* Flower and Teichert), Univ. Kansas, Pal. Contr., mollusca, art. 6, p. 140.

OCCURRENCE: One specimen (hypotype, G.S.C. No. 10801) from Member No. 1 of Caution Creek Formation, Churchill River: locality 25279

DESCRIPTION: Specimen referred to this species fragmentary but more complete than type specimen: approximately 70 mm long and divided almost equally between living chamber and phragmocone. In phragmocone five camerae preserved. Dorsoventral and lateral diameters 45 mm (estimated) and 37 mm, respectively, at base of phragmocone. At base of living chamber corresponding measurements 39 mm and 33 mm. Ventral wall of chamber not preserved. Dorsal wall strongly convex. In lateral profile chamber appears sharply contracted orad, as does that of holotype.

Hypotype evidently mature because sutures of lowest four camerae about 6 mm apart, whereas those of uppermost camera 4 mm apart. Sutures form broadly rounded lateral lobes and well-defined dorsal and ventral saddles. Bottoms of lobes about 1½ camerae below tops of corresponding saddles.

DISCUSSION: The type specimen is from the Shamattawa Formation of Gods River, Manitoba.

Winnipegoceras callahani sp. nov.
(Pl. 24, fig. 1)

OCCURRENCE: One specimen (holotype, G.S.C. No. 10550) from Member No. 2 of Chasm Creek Formation, Churchill River: locality 25285

DESCRIPTION: Holotype internal mold approximately 370 mm long, measured along convex ventral side, of which about 125 mm belongs to living chamber and remainder to phragmocone. In latter, estimated 22 camerae preserved. Convexity of ventral outline increases moderately from lower end of conch and reaches maximum about 130 mm below base of living chamber. Curvature gradually diminishes above here so that ventral outline of chamber only slightly convex. Dorsal outline roughly follows that of ventral, and maximum concavity approximately opposite maximum convexity on ventral side. Dorsoventral diameter 45 mm and lateral 15 mm (estimated) at lowest preserved part of phragmocone. Conch walls slowly diverge adorally until they reach maximum diameters at position about 75 mm, or 6 camerae, below living chamber. Dorsoventral diameter 75 mm here and lateral diameter 44 mm. Adorally there is a slight contraction and at base of living chamber corresponding two measurements 68 mm and 41 mm. Living chamber contracts toward aperture, and at highest preserved part dorsoventral diameter 50 mm (estimated) and lateral 22 mm.

In upper part of phragmocone, where sutures preserved, average depth of camerae about 10 mm. Camera immediately below living chamber, however, has depth of only 4 mm and suggests animal nearly full grown. Sutures form broadly rounded shallow lateral lobes having depth equivalent to that of about 1¼ camerae. They curve upward, both dorsally and ventrally, to form small, rounded saddles.

Structure of siphuncle unknown.

DISCUSSION: This species is most closely allied to *Winnipegoceras laticurvatum* (Whiteaves). The latter, however, is much smaller and has a proportionally larger lateral diameter in comparison with the dorsoventral diameter. *Winnipegoceras callahani* is distinguished from the Dog Head species *W. dowlingi* Foerste in that it is not so strongly curved lengthwise, and from the Shamattawa *W. contractum* (Foerste and Savage) in that it is larger and does not possess the strong orad contraction of the living chamber nor the marked lengthwise curvature.

The species is named in honor of Mr. J. Callahan, technician for the Geological Survey of Canada.

Family CYRTOGOMPHOCERATIDAE Flower
Genus *Cyrtogomphoceras* Foerste, 1924
Type Species: *Oncoceras magnum* Whiteaves, 1890

This genus contains endogastric breviconic or cyrtoceraconic conchs in which the maximum width, in mature individuals, is at the base of the living chamber or slightly below it. The chamber is somewhat contracted orad. The dorsal side of most specimens is uniformly convex, but that of a few is nearly angulate some distance below the living chamber; and the ventral side is nearly straight or slightly concave in longitudinal profile. A convex aspect is in some individuals imparted to the latter side by a gibbosity extending a short distance above and below the base of the living chamber. The transverse outline is circular or subelliptical, with the dorsoventral diameter forming the major axis.

Sutures are nearly transverse adapically but adorally rise from ventral to dorsal side and become progressively more oblique.

The siphuncle is large, ventral, and composed of nummuloidal segments, wide in comparison to their length.

Cyrtogomphoceras turgidum Troedsson
(Pl. 29, fig. 1)

1926 *Cyrtogomphoceras turgidum* TROEDSSON, Medd. om Grønland, v. 71, p. 97, Pl. 2, fig. 2; Pl. 57, figs. 1, 2; Pl. 58, figs. 2–4
1935 [?] *Cyrtogomphoceras vicinum* FOERSTE, Denison Univ. Bull., Jour. Sci. Lab., v. 30, p. 76, Pl. 14, fig. 2
1957 [?] *Cyrtogomphoceras vicinum* Foerste. FLOWER (*in* Flower and Teichert), Univ. Kansas Pal. Contr., mollusca, art. 6, p. 65

OCCURRENCE: Four specimens from Member No. 2 of Portage Chute Formation. One is from Nelson River: locality 25257; two from Churchill River: locality 25275; and one from South Knife River: locality 25299

Hypotype, G.S.C. No. 10508: Member No. 2, Portage Chute Formation, Churchill River, locality 25275
Hypotype, G.S.C. No. 10547: Member No. 2, Portage Chute Formation, Nelson River, locality 25257

DESCRIPTION: Four specimens referred to this species internal molds. Hypotype No. 10547 best preserved, but because one of lateral sides missing, lateral measurements must be estimated. Longitudinal dorsoventral profile very similar to that of type specimen. Hypotype about 117 mm long; about 70 mm belongs to living chamber (ventral side) and remainder to phragmocone. In latter, 10 camerae preserved. Dorsoventral diameter 30 mm, and lateral 26 mm at base of phragmocone. Maximum diameters occur about 4 camerae below dorsal base of living chamber where they are 68 mm and 56 mm, respectively. Adorally, specimen contracts gradually so that at aperture dorsoventral measurement 40 mm and lateral 27 mm.

Sutures approximately transverse in lower part of phragmocone. Adorally, slope from ventral to dorsal side becomes steeper so that uppermost suture makes horizontal angle of approximately 30°. Lateral sutures about 10 mm apart. Septa concave, and depth of curvature approximately equal to length of 1–1½ camerae.

South Knife River specimen, although not as complete as that from Nelson River shows details of siphuncle and transverse outline more clearly. This outline nearly elliptical and dorsoventral diameter is longer. Where dorsoventral measurement 36 mm, siphuncle 1 mm from ventral conch wall and has diameter, at passage through septum, of 7 mm. It enlarges between septa to about 15 mm. At dorsoventral diameter of 65 mm, siphuncle 4 mm from ventral wall and has corresponding measurements of 13 mm (estimated) and 24 mm.

DISCUSSION: The Churchill River specimens are questionably referred to *C. turgidum*. They do not have the well-defined ventral gibbosity near the base of the living chamber and have a nearly circular transverse outline. In many respects they are similar to *C. whiteavesi* (Miller).

The maximum dorsoventral and lateral conch diameters, given by Troedsson (1926) for the holotype from the Cape Calhoun Series of northern Greenland, are 60 mm and 54 mm, respectively. *Cyrtogomphoceras vicinum* Foerste, from the Lander Sandstone Member of the Bighorn Formation, Wyoming, is very similar in shape to *C. turgidum* but is proportionally larger. The corresponding maximum diameters given by Foerste (1935) for his species are 71 mm and 66 mm. The dorsoventral and lateral measurements of the Nelson River *C. turgidum* are intermediate between those of the types of these two species. The writer considers that *C. vicinum* is conspecific with *C. turgidum* and is questionably placing it in synonymy.

Cyrtogomphoceras nutatum Foerste and Savage
(Pl. 35, fig. 2)

1927 *Cyrtogomphoceras nutatum* FOERSTE and SAVAGE, Denison Univ. Bull., Jour. Sci. Lab., v. 22 p. 87, Pl. 17, figs. 2A, B
1957 *Cyrtogomphoceras nutatum* Foerste and Savage. FLOWER (*in* Flower and Teichert) Univ. Kansas, Pal. Contr., Mollusca, art. 6, p. 62, Pl. 6, figs. 3, 4; Pl. 7, figs. 1–3

OCCURRENCE: One specimen (hypotype, G.S.C. No. 10524) from Member No. 2 of Portage Chute Formation, Churchill River: locality 25271

DESCRIPTION: Churchill River specimen larger than type specimen, but shape similar. It is about 200 mm long, and maximum dorsoventral and lateral diameters occur about five camerae below dorsal base of living chamber where they are 77 mm and 107 mm, respectively.

DISCUSSION: The size of Churchill River *C. nutatum* and that of *C. magnum* (Whiteaves) of the Selkirk Member (= Dog Head) of the Red River Formation are almost the same and the two are strikingly similar in other ways. However, where *C. magnum* is more or less obliquely compressed laterally, *C. nutatum* is depressed dorsoventrally. It is not known if the elliptical section of these specimens is original or due to post depositional compaction. Because the Churchill River specimen is most closely related to *C. nutatum* the writer is referring it to that species.

The primary type is from Member No. 2 of the Portage Chute Formation (formerly Nelson River Formation), Nelson River. It was probably collected at locality 25258.

Cyrtogomphoceras rotundum Miller
(Pl. 23, fig. 2)

1932 *Cyrtogomphoceras rotundum* MILLER, Trans. Connecticut Acad. Arts Sci., v. 31, p. 294, Pl. 30, fig. 1; Pl. 31, fig.1
1935 *Cyrtogomphoceras rotundum* MILLER. FOERSTE, Denison Univ. Bull., Jour. Sci. Lab., v. 30, p. 76, Pl. 14, fig. 1
1957 *Cyrtogomphoceras rotundum* Miller. FLOWER (*in* Flower and Teichert), Univ. Kansas, Pal. Contr., Mollusca, art. 6, p. 64

OCCURRENCE: One specimen (hypotype, G.S.C. No. 10546) from Member No. 2 of Portage Chute Formation, South Knife River: locality 25299

DESCRIPTION: South Knife River specimen internal mold 130 mm long, measured along ventral side, of which approximately 70 mm belongs to living chamber and remainder to phragmocone. It is nearly identical in lateral and dorsoventral longitudinal outline with holotype illustrated by Miller but larger and somewhat dorsoventrally depressed. At preserved base of specimen, 14 camerae below living chamber, dorsoventral diameter 42 mm and lateral 44 mm. Maximum diameters occur in horizontal plane intersecting fourth camera below living chamber on ventral side and seventh on dorsal side. Here dorsoventral and lateral measurements 66 mm and 80 mm, respectively. Above this place conch gradually contracts and at aperture corresponding diameters 30 mm (estimated) and 45 mm. Faint longitudinal grooves, about 2 mm apart, occur along one of the dorsolateral surfaces of phragmocone. Similar grooves also present on specimen of *C. rotundum* illustrated by Foerste (1935), but he did not mention them.

Adapical sutures approximately transverse and about 7 mm apart on dorsal and 4 mm on ventral side. Adorally they gradually become farther apart and slope progressively upward from ventral to dorsal side so that uppermost suture makes horizontal angle of about 35° with axis. Sutures about 4 mm apart on ventral and 12 mm on dorsal side near living chamber. Most adoral camera decidedly shallower than lower ones and indicates that specimen mature. Sutures of this camera about 4 mm apart on dorsal side.

DISCUSSION: The specimens described by Miller (1932) and Foerste (1935) are from the Lander Sandstone Member of the Bighorn Formation, Wyoming.

Cyrtogomphoceras baffinense Foerste

1928 *Cyrtogomphoceras baffinense* FOERSTE, Contr. Mus. Pal., Univ. Michigan, v. 3, no. 3, p. 63, Pl. 4, fig. 1; Pl. 11, fig. 4
1928 [?] *Cyrtogomphoceras* cf. *C. baffinense* Foerste. FOERSTE, Contr. Mus. Pal., Univ. Michigan v. 3, no. 3, p. 65, Pl. 4, fig. 2
1941 [*non*] *Cyrtogomphoceras baffinense* Foerste. ROY, Field Mus. Nat. Hist. Geol. Mem., v. 2, p. 147, fig. 107
1954 *Cyrtogomphoceras baffinense* Foerste. MILLER, YOUNGQUIST, and COLLINSON, Geol. Soc. America Mem. 62, p. 105, Pl. 43, fig. 6; Pl. 53, figs. 1–3
1957 *Cyrtogomphoceras baffinense* Foerste. FLOWER (*in* Flower and Teichert), Univ. Kansas Pal. Contr., Mollusca, art. 6, p. 63
1957 *Cyrtogomphoceras baffinense* Foerste. SWEET and MILLER, Geol. Surv. Canada Bull. 38, p. 51, fig. 91, Pl. 5, figs. 7, 8

OCCURRENCE: One specimen (hypotype, G.S.C. No. 10543) from Member No. 2 of Portage Chute Formation, Churchill River: locality 25272

DESCRIPTION: Churchill River specimen well-preserved internal mold very similar in most characteristics to holotype. It is about 100 mm long, measured along ventral side, of which 70 mm belongs to phragmocone and remainder to living chamber. Ventral outline nearly straight and has slight concavity near upper part of living chamber. Dorsal surface uniformly convex and has radius of curvature of approximately 70 mm. Lateral sides somewhat distorted but originally probably uniformly convex. Transverse outline subelliptical and dorsoventral diameter larger. At preserved base of specimen, 10 camerae below living chamber, dorsoventral and lateral diameters 40 mm and 30 mm (estimated), respectively. Maximum diameters occur at about same level as horizontal plane passing through ventral base of living chamber and intersecting dorsal surface about 5 camerae below this chamber. Dorsoventral diameter here, 60 mm and lateral diameter 48 mm. Corresponding two diameters 42 mm and 33 mm at about 40 mm above ventral base of this chamber.

Sutures of Churchill River specimen similar to those of holotype but slightly more widely spaced, and adoral sutures do not form lateral lobes. They are about 6–7 mm apart along median-lateral sides, where Foerste's figure of holotype shows cameral depth of 5 mm. Adorally they slope progressively upward from ventral to dorsal side so that uppermost suture makes horizontal angle with axis of about 45°. Both holotype and hypotype mature individuals, because uppermost camera decidedly shallower than lower camerae.

DISCUSSION: The holotype of *C. baffinense* was collected from "...Putman Highland, Baffin Island, in strata corresponding to the Red River formation of southern Manitoba." (Foerste, 1928, p. 64).

Cyrtogomphoceras thompsoni Miller and Furnish
(Pl. 26, fig. 1)

1937 *Cyrtogomphoceras thompsoni* MILLER and FURNISH, Jour. Pal., v. 11, no. 7, p. 549, Pl. 68, fig. 3
1944 *Cyrtogomphoceras thompsoni* Miller and Furnish. SHIMER and SHROCK, Index Fossils of North America, p. 561, Pl. 230, fig. 14
1957 *Cyrtogomphoceras thompsoni* Miller and Furnish. FLOWER (*in* Flower and Teichert), Univ. Kansas, Pal. Contr., Mollusca, art. 6, p. 65

OCCURRENCE: Two specimens from Member No. 2 of Portage Chute Formation. One (hypotype, G.S.C. No. 10792) is from Churchill River: locality 25275; and the other (hypotype, G.S.C. No. 10545) from Nelson River: locality 25254

DESCRIPTION: Both specimens internal molds and almost identical with holotype.

Nelson River specimen better preserved. Mold about 190 mm long, measured along median-lateral sides, of which about 110 mm phragmocone and remainder living chamber. Former has 14–15 preserved camerae. Transverse outline elliptical, and dorsoventral diameter is larger. Dorsal side evenly convex over length of specimen in longitudinal profile. Ventral slightly concave along lower end, nearly straight along upper part of phragmocone and lower two-thirds of living chamber and curved rather sharply above here. Maximum dorsoventral diameters occur between four and five camerae below living chamber, measured along dorsal side, and approximately at same elevation as horizontal plane passing through ventral base of chamber. Specimen enlarges gradually orad in lateral outline, attains maximum diameter where dorsoventral diameter largest, and then narrows orad rather gradually. At preserved base of specimen, dorsoventral diameter 30 mm, and corresponding lateral diameter 25 mm (estimated). Corresponding two diameters 68 mm and 56 mm at position of greatest width. At uppermost preserved portion of living chamber dorsoventral and lateral diameters 42 mm (estimated) and 31 mm, respectively.

Adapically, sutures nearly transverse but adorally they curve progressively higher from ventral to dorsal side. Uppermost suture makes horizontal angle of approximately 30°. Ventral sutures about 4 mm apart; lateral ones about 8 mm; and dorsal sutures 10–12 mm apart.

Churchill River specimen approximately 180 mm long, measured along median-lateral sides, of which 120 mm phragmocone and 60 mm living chamber. Fourteen camerae preserved. Shape almost identical with that of holotype. Dorsoventral diameter 53 mm and lateral diameter 34 mm (estimated), at base of specimen. Greatest diameters between five and six camerae below living chamber, measured along dorsal side, where these two measurements 75 mm and 51 mm, respectively. Corresponding measurements 68 mm and 52 mm at base of chamber.

DISCUSSION: The only notable difference between the holotype of *C. thompsoni* from the dolomite member of the Whitewood Formation, South Dakota, and northern Manitoban specimens is that the uppermost sutures of the former make well-defined shallow lateral lobes. They tend to be nearly straight or only slightly concave in the present specimens.

The writer has examined the type specimen of *C. intermedium* (Whiteaves) from the Dog Head Member of the Red River Formation. It is very similar to *C. thompsoni*. It differs from the latter in having a slightly but evenly concave ventral outline, whereas in *C. thompsoni* the ventral outline along the adoral 18–19 camerae is very slightly humped or nearly straight.

Cyrtogomphoceras foerstei Miller and Furnish
(Pl. 27, fig. 1)

1937 *Cyrtogomphoceras foerstei* MILLER and FURNISH, Jour. Pal., v. 11, no. 7, p. 548, Pl. 68, figs. 1, 2
1957 *Cyrtogomphoceras foerstei* Miller and Furnish. FLOWER (*in* Flower and Teichert), Univ. Kansas, Pal. Contr., Mollusca, art. 6, p. 65

OCCURRENCE: One specimen (hypotype, G.S.C. No. 10544) from Member No. 2 of Portage Chute Formation, South Knife River: locality 25297

DESCRIPTION: Miller and Furnish (1937) based this species on single internal mold from dolomite member of Whitewood Formation, South Dakota. South Knife River specimen also internal mold, of which one of lateral sides missing. In over-all dimensions three-tenths larger than holotype: about 200 mm long; 80 mm is living chamber and remainder phragmocone. Phragmocone has 15 preserved camerae. Dorsoventral and lateral diameters 32 mm and 17 mm at base of phragmocone. About five camerae below dorsal base of living chamber, where specimen widest, these diameters 77 mm and 52 mm (estimated), respectively. Corresponding two measurements 67 mm and 48 mm at base of chamber.

Sutures have approximately same pattern and spacing as those on holotype. On dorsal side about 9–10 mm apart adapically and 10–12 mm apart adorally.

Cyrtogomphoceras alcocki sp. nov.
(Pl. 28, figs. 1a, b)

OCCURRENCE: Two specimens from Member No. 2 of Portage Chute Formation. The holotype (G.S.C No. 10541) is from Nelson River; locality 25257; and the paratype (G.S.C. No. 10542) from Churchill River: locality 25272

DESCRIPTION: Holotype and paratype nearly identical internal molds. Former better preserved: about 100 mm long; 55 mm living chamber, measured along median-lateral sides, and remainder phragmocone. In latter nine camerae preserved. Transverse outline elliptical, and dorsoventral diameter is longer. Ventral side nearly straight in longitudinal outline but slightly gibbous for about 15 mm above base of living chamber. Dorsal side strongly convex, almost angular and maximum curvature 4–5 camerae below living chamber and approximately opposite ventral base of chamber. At preserved base of phragmocone dorsoventral and lateral diameters 40 mm and 33 mm, respectively. Maximum diameters occur where dorsal convexity greatest. Here, corresponding measurements 66 mm and 44 mm. Dorsoventral and lateral diameters 40 mm and 27 mm, respectively, at aperture. Marked ventral hyponomic sinus, about 10 mm deep, present.

Apicad sutures approximately transverse. Adorally they gradually rise higher from ventral to dorsal side, so that uppermost suture very weakly lobed laterally, and makes horizontal angle of about 30°. They are about 3 mm, 5 mm, and 8 mm apart on ventral, lateral, and dorsal sides, respectively.

DISCUSSION: *Cyrtogomphoceras alcocki* appears closest to *C. curvatum* Troedsson from the Cape Calhoun Series of northern Greenland in its markedly rounded longitudinal dorsal profile and transverse outline. However, the dorsal profile is less convex, and the ventral is nearly straight with a slight gibbosity above the base of the living chamber.

The species is named in honor of Dr. F. J. Alcock who descended the Churchill River in 1914.

Order BARRANDEOCERATIDA Flower
Family PLECTOCERATIDAE Hyatt
Genus *Antiplectoceras* Foerste and Savage
Type Species: *Discoceras*(?) *shamattawaense* Parks, 1915

The conch is nautiliform, slowly enlarging, and whorls are in contact but not appressed. In early growth stages whorls are subcircular to oval in cross section, but in later stages formation of an acute ventral ridge gives them a tear-drop outline.

The surface is transversely ornamented by coarse ribs curving apicad laterally and orad dorsally and ventrally. Sutures parallel ribs and one occurs in each of the intervening depressions.

The siphuncle is ventral and cyrtochoanitic.

This description is based on the single species *A. shamattawaense*. The genus appears closely related to *Discoceras* but can be distinguished in that the ribs form lateral "lobes" and dorsal and ventral "saddles".

As will be discussed below the genus *Goniotrochoceras* Foerste is here considered synonymous with *Antiplectoceras*.

Antiplectoceras shamattawaense (Parks)
(Pl. 31, fig. 3)

1913 *Trochoceras insigne* Whiteaves. PARKS (*in* Tyrrell), Bur. Mines Ontario, 22d Rept., pt. 1, p. 192
1915 *Discoceras*(?) *shamattawaense* PARKS, Trans. Roy. Canadian Inst., v. 11, p. 31, Pl. 1, fig. 1
1927 *Antiplectoceras shamattawaense* (Parks). FOERSTE and SAVAGE, Denison Univ. Bull., Jour. Sci. Lab., v. 22, p. 58, Pl. 24, fig. 2
1928 [?] *Goniotrochoceras twenhofeli* FOERSTE (*in* Twenhofel), Geol. Surv. Canada Mem. 154, p. 285, Pl. 38, figs. 1, 2
1943 *Antiplectoceras shamattawaense* (Parks). OKULITCH, Trans. Roy. Soc. Canada, v. 37, sec. 4, Pl. 2, figs. 4, 5
1947a *Discoceras?* sp. MILLER and YOUNGQUIST, Jour. Pal., v. 21, no. 1, p. 15, Pl. 5, fig. 4

OCCURRENCE: Four specimens from Member No. 3 of Chasm Creek Formation, Churchill River: locality 25290. The species appears to be characteristic of this horizon.

Hypotypes, G.S.C. No. 10552, 10553

DESCRIPTION: Two specimens referred to this species nearly complete molds of whorls but dolomitized to such an extent that only surface features distinguishable. Other two fairly well preserved whorl fragments and best preserved one (hypotype No. 10553), which has given information about internal structures, consists of three adjacent whorls. Following description of *A. shamattawaense* based on above four specimens.

Conch nautiliform, slowly enlarging, and whorls in contact but not appressed. Up to third volution transverse whorl shape subcircular to oval. Adorally from here ventrolateral sides converge and form acute longitudinal ventral ridge. At progressively orad positions where whorls have dorsoventral diameters of 6 mm, 16 mm and 26 mm respectively, corresponding lateral measurements 5 mm, 12 mm, and 16 mm. Ventral ridge present at last position. Adorally whorls increase in size both dorsoventrally and laterally so that measurements of these diameters at any one position approximately double corresponding measurements taken on immediately adjacent part of inner whorl.

Surface transversely ornamented by lobelike ribs curving apicad laterally and arising orad both dorsally and ventrally. These ribs most pronounced on lateral surfaces and become low and rounded on ventral and dorsal slopes. Distance between them, measured on middle of lateral sides, about a fourth that of dorsoventral diameter at same place.

One suture occurs in depressions between ribs and forms lateral lobes and dorsal and ventral saddles. Septa curved dorsoventrally but nearly straight laterally. Viewed adorally or adapically in outer whorls, they present tear-drop appearance, the sharp tip being formed by oblique junction of septa with ventral ridge. Maximum dorsoventral curvature of septa about equal to depth of one camera in outer whorls. In inner whorls, however, curvature less because ribs and alternating septa slope laterally downward less rapidly than in later growth stages.

Siphuncle ventral, cyrtochoanitic, apparently hollow and slightly swollen between septa so that it resembles string of sausages. Approximately 4 mm from ventral wall and has maximum width of 2 mm where dorsoventral whorl diameter 27 mm (estimated). Dorsal side of connecting rings very slightly convex dorsally. Ventral side convex ventrally and maximum curvature occurs in upper half toward septal neck. Dorsal part of septal neck recurved until it makes angle of 70°–80° with septa, whereas ventral portion makes angle of approximately 90°.

DISCUSSION: Foerste (*in* Twenhofel, 1928) described the new genus and species *Goniotrochoceras twenhofeli* based on a whorl fragment from the Vaureal Formation of Anticosti Island. The specimen, which consists of a living chamber and two camerae, was thought to have been spirally coiled because of the slight similarity in transverse whorl shape between it and representatives of the helicoid genus *Mitroceras*. Although Foerste thought it probable that the shell coiled spirally, he noted that the specimen shows no evidence of it. From his description it would appear that the transverse outline of the whorl is nearly tear-drop-shaped, and the tip represents the acute outer ventral margin. This margin is slightly off center. A longitudinal furrow, about 8 mm wide, runs along one side of it.

The surface of *G. twenhofeli* is ornamented by transverse lobelike ribs alternating with sutures. In their pattern and spacing these structures are almost identical with those of *A. shamattawaense*. The only noticeable difference is that the surface of the former species is covered by rather closely spaced raised longitudinal striae. It is not known if *A. shamattawaense* ever had such striae. The specimen illustrated by Okulitch (1943), however, shows very faint longitudinal markings suggestive of those of *G. twenhofeli.*

Little can be said at present about the longitudinal furrow. It may be of generic or specific significance, or possibly formed by postburial compaction. *Goniotrochoceras* may be congeneric with *Antiplectoceras.* Because *G. twenhofeli* is so similar in appearance to *A. shamattawaense* the writer is provisionally referring it to that species.

Miller and Youngquist (1947a) described a specimen from Sutton Island which they referred to *Discoceras* sp. The writer has examined it and found it almost identical with the northern Manitoban specimens here referred to *A. shamattawaense.*

If the foregoing discussion of synonymy is correct then *A. shamattawaense* has a rather wide geographic range as it occurs in Manitoba, Anticosti Island, and Sutton Island. The primary type is from the Shamattawa Formation of Gods River, northern Manitoba (Parks, 1915; Foerste and Savage, 1927). Okulitch (1943) has identified it from the Gunton Member (Birse interval) of the Stony Mountain Formation in southern Manitoba. Baillie (1951) and Stearn (1956) indicated that it also occurs in the overlying Stonewall Formation which Stearn (1956) considered to be Ordovician.

Family APSIDOCERATIDAE Hyatt

Genus *Fremontoceras* Foerste, 1935

Type Species: *Fremontoceras loperi* Foerste, 1935

Foerste's (1935, p. 89) diagnosis of this genus is as follows:

"Conch coiled, possibly gyroceraconic; at least there is no indication of contact between successive volutions; enlarging rapidly, only a part of the phragmocone being known. Cross section subquadrangular, with a slight flattening of the lateral sides and a more distinct flattening of the ventral one, resulting in a tendency toward angulation ventrolaterally. The sutures of the septa rise slightly toward these ventrolateral angles, and then curve distinctly downward ventrally, resulting in ventrolateral saddles and ventral lobes, the latter being only of moderate depth. The siphuncle is located ventrad of the center of the conch. . . ."

Features considered diagnostic for this genus are the flattened ventral side and sutures with ventrolateral saddles and ventral lobes. Although poorly preserved, the Churchill River specimen referred to this genus shows that the conch is nautilicone and not gyroceraconic.

Besides the type species, two other species have been referred to *Fremontoceras.* These are *F. jewetti* Flower and *F. gigantea* Flower, from the Trentonian of New York and Quebec, respectively. In the writer's opinion neither may belong in this genus because they do not have pronounced ventral lobes nor ventrolateral saddles. The only feature, apparently, they have in common with the genotype is the flattened ventral side. The last feature may not be sufficiently important to warrant placing them in *Fremontoceras.*

Fremontoceras sp., cf. *F. loperi* Foerste

1935 *Fremontoceras loperi* FOERSTE, Denison Univ. Bull., Jour. Sci. Lab., v. 30, p. 89, Pl. 19, figs. 1–4.

OCCURRENCE: One specimen from Member No. 1 of Chasm Creek Formation, Churchill River: locality 25283

DESCRIPTION: Specimen compared with this species is fragmentary internal mold containing 3–3½ volutions and having maximum diameter of 145 mm. One of lateral sides of whorls destroyed, and no internal structures visible.

Estimated dorsoventral and lateral diameters at assumed base of living chamber, 150 mm below top of specimen, 45 mm and 60 mm, respectively. Estimates for other whorl positions cannot be made because of fragmentary nature of specimen. Ventral side on outer whorl very slightly convex.

Adoral sutures partially preserved. They show well-defined ventral lobes and ventrolateral saddles, characteristic of genus, and are about 11 mm apart on ventral, and 8 mm on lateral surface.

DISCUSSION: In size, shape, and pattern and spacing of sutures the Churchill River specimen is very similar to the type specimen of *F. loperi* from the Fremont Formation of Colorado. Because of the fragmentary nature of the former specimen, however, the writer does not think it advisable either to erect a new species or definitely refer it to *F. loperi* until more material is available for study.

Genus *Apsidoceras* Hyatt, 1884

Type Species: *Gyroceras (Lituites) magnificum* Billings, 1857

This genus contains rather large, gyroceraconic shells with the ventral side strongly flattened so so that the transverse whorl outline is subtriagonal or semicircular. Two broad shallow marginal furrows, one on each side of the median-ventral line, are present in many individuals and extend the ventral conch length. The shell surface may be smooth or ornamented.

Sutures form broad shallow ventral lobes, small ventrolateral saddles, and dorsal saddles.

The siphuncle is ventral and nummuloidal.

Apsidoceras boreale Foerste and Savage
(Pl. 33, fig. 2)

1927 *Apsidoceras boreale* FOERSTE and SAVAGE, Denison Univ. Bull., Jour. Sci. Lab., v. 22, p. 60, Pl. 14, figs. 1A, B, C

OCCURRENCE: One specimen (hypotype, G.S.C. No. 10504) from the Chasm Creek Formation, Nelson River: locality 25269

DESCRIPTION: Hypotype adoral portion of whorl about 220 mm long, measured along ventral side. Living chamber probably about 165 mm and remainder phragmocone with four camerae. Ventral surface has longitudinal radius of curvature of about 155 mm and flat to slightly convex transverse outline. Dorsal and dorsolateral sides rather highly convex and join ventral side approximately at right angles to form narrowly rounded margins. Specimen enlarges orad slowly and uniformly, and dorsoventral diameter in all specimens slightly smaller than lateral. At preserved base of specimen, two diameters 41 mm and 47 mm, respectively and at 90 mm above base of living chamber, 45 mm and 54 mm.

Sutures about 11 mm apart along ventral side and about 8 mm along dorsal. Their pattern similar to that of type specimen. Septa deeply concave, their depth equal to that of 1½ camerae.

Siphuncle has diameter of about 4 mm at passage through septum and located about 18 mm from ventral wall.

DISCUSSION: The type specimen of *A. boreale* is from the Shamattawa Formation of Gods River, northern Manitoba.

Apsidoceras milleri sp. nov.
(Pl. 33, fig. 1; Pl. 34, figs. 1a, b)

OCCURRENCE: One specimen (holotype, G.S.C. No. 10520) from Member No. 1 of Chasm Creek Formation, Churchill River: locality 25283

DESCRIPTION: Holotype well-preserved internal mold about 310 mm in ventral length, of which about 60 mm (estimated) living chamber and remainder phragmocone. Plaster cast (plastoholotype, G.S.C. No. 10521) has been made of holotype. Latter sectioned, but no trace of septa or siphuncle found.

Specimen curved lengthwise, and ventral side has radius of curvature approximately 290 mm. Transverse whorl outline semielliptical and dorsoventral diameter in most specimens ranges from a third to a half that of lateral. Middle of dorsal side slightly convex, becomes rather strongly curved dorsolaterally, and meets ventral surface nearly at right angles to form narrowly rounded margins. Ventral side almost flat. Near margin two broad, shallow longitudinal furrows, 2–3 mm deep and each between 20–30 mm wide, extend length of specimen. Median part of ventral surface, between furrows, very slightly convex. Specimen gradually expands orad both dorsoventrally and laterally. At about 15 camerae below base of living chamber, or distance of approximately 165 mm, measured along ventro-lateral sides, dorsoventral diameter 50 mm and corresponding lateral diameter 132 mm.

Corresponding measurements 65 mm and 140 mm at base of this chamber. Part of mold covered with altered shell material: on ventral surface between 1 and 2 mm thick, but thickening to nearly 5 mm at ventrolateral margins.

Approximately 14 camerae occur in distance equal to lateral diameter of conch. Sutures uniformly spaced and about 8 mm apart on middle of dorsal and 14 mm apart on middle of ventral side. They cross ventral surface as broadly rounded lobes, and depth equal to length of about three camerae. Sutures form narrowly rounded ventrolateral saddles and swing sharply downward over dorsolateral slopes as lobes which decrease in curvature as they approach middle of dorsal side. Depth of these lobes equivalent to that of 4½–5 camerae. On middle of dorsal surface they form slightly angulated saddles, height of which about half length of camera.

DISCUSSION: *Apsidoceras milleri* appears to be closest to *A. depressum* Cooper, but is larger and has shallower camerae and deeper ventral lobes. It has shallower camerae and is more depressed than *A. magnificum* (Billings), *A. boreale* Foerste and Savage, and *A. elegans* Troedsson.

Apsidoceras milleri is named in honor of Dr. A. K. Miller of the State University of Iowa.

Genus *Charactoceras* Foerste, 1924
Type Species: *Trochoceras ? Baeri* Meek and Worthen, 1865

Flower (1946, p. 488–489) and Miller, Youngquist, and Collinson (1954, p. 112–113) have discussed this genus in detail. The latter authors' diagnosis was:

"Forms that belong in this genus have thickly subdiscoidal nautiliconic conchs in which whorls are rapidly expanded, considerably wider than high, distinctly impressed dorsally, and therefore reniform in cross section. Umbilicus moderate in size, and umbilical shoulders broadly rounded. Growth lines indicate that aperture bore a deep rounded hyponomic sinus. Each suture forms a broad shallow rounded ventral saddle and similar but narrower lateral and dorsal lobes separated by rather prominent dorso-lateral saddles. Siphuncle, located fairly close to venter, is composed of subfusiform segments."

Charactoceras manitobense sp. nov.
(Pl. 19, fig. 2; Pl. 30, fig. 4)

OCCURRENCE: Two specimens from Member No. 2 of Portage Chute Formation. The holotype (G.S.C. No. 10860) is from South Knife River: locality 25299; and the paratype (G.S.C. No. 10885) from Churchill River: locality 25272

DESCRIPTION: Holotype well-preserved internal mold on which some altered shell material still adheres. One lateral side of outer volution missing. Specimen has maximum diameter of 122 mm, and consists of 2½–3 volutions of which last 90 mm, measured along ventral side, living chamber. About 250 mm from most orad part of specimen, measured along ventral side, dorsoventral and lateral diameters 27 mm and 40 mm (estimated), respectively. This position is on inner whorl adjacent to most adapical part of outer one and considered approximately 1½–2 volutions from apex. Adorally from here dorsoventral diameter increases slowly, but lateral enlarges rather rapidly. Dorsoventral and lateral diameters 46 mm and 66 mm (estimated), respectively, at uppermost part of living chamber. Volutions cover about a third of adjacent inner whorl so that there is distinct impressed zone. Part of ventral surface, between 1 to ½ volution from top covered with poorly preserved altered shell material on which striae, about 1 mm apart, indicate positions of broadly rounded hyponomic sinuses. Each sinus estimated to have been 10–15 mm deep.

Sutures approximately transverse in early growth stages but later form ventral lobes; spaced about 2.5 mm on lateral sides and about 4–5 mm on ventral at about one volution from top. They gradually increase in spacing orad and, near living chamber, are about 5 mm apart laterally and 8–9 mm ventrally. Septa gently concave, depth of curvature equivalent to length of one camera.

Siphuncle suborthochoanitic and preserved at about three quarters volution from adoral part of conch. Ventral wall approximately 5–6 mm from that of phragmocone. It has diameter of 2 mm at passage through septum. Between septa it enlarges slightly to diameter of about 3 mm.

Paratype No. 10885 portion of phragmocone broken about 2 volutions from adapical end of conch: about 110 mm long, measured along ventral side. Adapical sutures approximately transverse but adorally form ventral lobes characteristic of species.

DISCUSSION: *Charactoceras manitobense* is most similar to *C. laddi* Foerste. The shape is almost identical with that of the paratype of *C. laddi* illustrated by Foerste (1936, Pl. 30, fig. 1). It differs from this and from all other described species in possessing sutures with well-defined ventral lobes in mature stages.

In possessing ventral lobes, *C. manitobense* is very similar to the genus *Fremontoceras* Foerste. The ventral side of the former, however, is gently curved in transverse outline whereas that of the latter is flattened.

Charactoceras laddi Foerste
(Pl. 28, fig. 3)

1936 *Charactoceras laddi* FOERSTE, Denison Univ. Bull., Jour. Sci. Lab., v. 30, p. 254, Pl. 30, figs. 1–3; Pl. 31, fig. 1

OCCURRENCE: Two specimens from Caution Creek Formation. One (hypotype, G.S.C. No. 10507) is from Member No. 1, Churchill River: locality 25281; and the other is from the Upper Member South Knife River: locality 24304

DESCRIPTION: Hypotype No. 10507 internal mold of phragmocone and living chamber with diameter of 130 mm. Adapical part of specimen rather poorly preserved. Upper 120 mm living chamber. Shape of specimen almost identical with that of paratype (*see* Foerste, 1936, Pl. 30, fig. 1) of *C. laddi*. Hypotype, however, larger individual, approximately 80 mm longer. It enlarges rather uniformly orad, both laterally and dorsoventrally. At about 15 camerae below living chamber, or approximately 175 mm measured along ventral side, dorsoventral and lateral diameters 30 mm and 40 mm (estimated), respectively. Corresponding two measurements 44 mm and 55 mm (estimated), at base of living chamber and at preserved top of chamber 54 mm and 68 mm (estimated), respectively.

Sutures rise higher ventrally than dorsally and form low, broadly rounded ventral saddles. On inner volution directly adjacent to that containing base of living chamber, sutures spaced between 7 and 8 mm along ventral wall and about 4 mm along lateral walls. Corresponding spacing 10 mm and 5 mm about 175 mm below base of living chamber. Toward chamber ventral spacing increases to 12 mm and lateral to 7 mm.

DISCUSSION: The holotype and paratypes of *C. laddi* are from the Elgin Member of the Maquoketa Formation, Iowa. The species appears to be most closely related to *C. schucherti* Foerste from Silliman's Fossil Mount in southern Baffin Island but differs in having more widely spaced sutures. There are also numerous similarities between *C. laddi* and *C. rotundum* Troedsson from the Cape Calhoun Series of northern Greenland. The latter species, however, has only a very weakly defined impressed zone.

Charactoceras warrenae sp. nov.
(Pl. 29, fig. 2; Pl. 37, figs. 1, 4)

OCCURRENCE: Two specimens from Member No. 1 of the Caution Creek Formation, Churchill River: localities 25281, 25282

Holotype, G.S.C. No. 10798: locality 25281
Paratype, G.S.C. No. 10506: locality 25282

DESCRIPTION: Holotype and paratype internal molds of adoral whorls.

Holotype larger and more complete specimen: whorl about 140 mm long, measured along ventral side, which is nearly semicircular in longitudinal ventral outline. Phragmocone about 100 mm long and consists of 10 camerae. Whorl gradually enlarges orad both dorsoventrally and laterally. At preserved base of phragmocone dorsoventral and lateral diameters 36 mm and 70 mm, respectively. At base of living chamber corresponding dimensions 40 mm and 84 mm; and at uppermost preserved part 45 mm and 95 mm. Transverse whorl outline laterally elongate with ventral side very gently convex and lateral sides nearly semicircular. Impressed zone well-developed, and its width about $\frac{4}{10}$ lateral diameter. It is relatively deeply concave, and maximum depth 4–6 mm.

Sutures nearly transverse; 8 mm apart along ventral; 4 mm along lateral; and 3 mm apart along dorsal side.

Paratype less complete than holotype and consists of living chamber and phragmocone with four preserved camerae. It does, however, have better preserved sutures. Whorl about 160 mm long, measured along ventral side. Of this length, 113 mm living chamber and remainder phragmocone. Estimated dorsoventral and lateral diameters 27 mm and 85 mm, respectively, at base of phragmocone. It enlarges uniformly orad and at base of living chamber corresponding two dimensions 44 mm and 92 mm. About 85 mm above base of chamber, dorsoventral diameter 50 mm (estimated) and lateral diameter 95 mm. Ventral wall very gently rounded in transverse outline. Lateral sides rather sharply rounded and maximum curvature nearer ventral than dorsal side. Inpressed zone not well preserved but appears to have been approximately 40 mm wide and 6 mm deep.

Sutures approximately transverse. Along ventral surface about 11 mm apart. Those of most orad camera 9 mm apart and suggest that specimen mature.

DISCUSSION: The holotype and paratype are similar in most essential respects. One important difference is that the latter is not so strongly convex in longitudinal ventral outline as the holotype. Until more specimens are available it cannot be stated whether or not this difference in curvature is of specific rank. For the present, however, they will be referred to the same species.

Charactoceras warrenae can be easily distinguished from other representatives of the genus by its relatively wide whorls. It appears similar to *C. hercules* (Billings) from the English Head and Vaureal formations of Anticosti Island. The writer has compared the types of *C. warrenae* with the holotype of the latter species. They are very similar in their rate of enlargement, spacing and pattern of sutures, and in having a large lateral to dorsoventral diameter ratio. Where the lateral diameter is 93 mm, in the holotype and paratype of *C. warrenae*, corresponding dorsoventral diameters are 45 mm and 44 mm, respectively. At the same lateral diameter, however, the holotype of *C. hercules* has a dorsoventral diameter of 53 mm.

Charactoceras warrenae is named in honor of Professor Althea Warren of the University of New Brunswick.

Genus *Charactocerina* Foerste, 1935
Type Species: *Eurystomites plicatus* Whiteaves, 1895

The genus *Charactocerina* is almost identical with *Charactoceras* Foerste, but differs in that the conch has transverse dorsolateral ribs. According to Miller, Youngquist, and Collinson (1954, p. 113) segments of the siphuncle are less expanded between septa than in *Charactoceras*.

Charactocerina kirki Foerste

1935 *Charactocerina kirki* FOERSTE, Denison Univ. Bull., Jour. Sci. Lab., v. 30, p. 86, Pl. 20, figs. 1–4

OCCURRENCE: One specimen (hypotype, G.S.C. No. 10861) from Member No. 1 of Portage Chute Formation, Churchill River: locality 25272

DESCRIPTION: Specimen referred to this species poorly preserved sandstone mold on which some altered shell material adheres toward apical end. Mold more complete than holotype: approximately 2–2½ volutions present, and last whorl becomes gyroconic in upper third volution. Living chamber about 170 mm long, measured along median-ventral side, comprises most of this last third of whorl.

Maximum diameter of specimen about 145 mm. Adapically, transverse whorl outline elliptical and lateral diameter is longer. Ratio of dorsoventral to lateral diameters decreases adorally. Adapically, transverse ventral outline broadly rounded but becomes increasingly flatter toward living chamber where it is only gently convex. Lateral wall at latter position almost semicircular. At distance of about 490 mm, or 1½ volutions from top of specimen, measured along median-ventral side, estimated dorsoventral and lateral diameters 20 mm and 26 mm, respectively. Corresponding two diameters 45 mm and 70 mm, at base of living chamber 340 mm orad, and at aperture 56 mm and 82 mm, respectively. Lateral surface of conch crossed by low rounded ribs about 2–3 mm high, which become fainter and disappear dorsally and ventrally. Ribs, about 8 mm apart, have ventral extremities directed adapically and dorsal ends adorally to make angles between 20° and 30° with sutures.

Sutures approximately transverse. They are about 7 mm apart on ventral side one volution from top. Adorally, over ventral distance of about 140 mm, spacing increases to about 9 mm and an estimated 5 mm laterally. Last position about 80 mm below base of living chamber. Toward chamber they decrease in spacing so that directly below base sutures about 5 mm apart ventrally and 2–3 mm apart laterally. Decrease in spacing suggests specimen mature.

DISCUSSION: The Churchill River specimen is very similar to the holotype of *Charactocerina kirki* from the Lander Sandstone Member of the Bighorn Formation, Wyoming. Although the former is somewhat distorted adapically, the reconstructed longitudinal outline and the ratios of dorsoventral to lateral diameters are very close to those of the holotype. Foerste (1935) noted the gyroconic coiling taking place in later growth stages of *C. kirki*.

Charactocerina goodwini sp. nov.
(Pl. 30, fig. 3; Pl. 32, fig. 4)

OCCURRENCE: One specimen (holotype, G.S.C. No. 10805) from Member No. 3 of Caution Creek Formation, Churchill River; locality 25280

DESCRIPTION: Holotype well-preserved internal mold of phragmocone probably consisting of 2–2½ volutions.

Conch nautiliform, tightly coiled, sharply expanding both dorsoventrally and laterally, and has maximum diameter of 60 mm. Transverse whorl outline on outer volutions nearly elliptical: lateral diameter the larger. At ventral distance of 140 mm below most adoral part of phragmocone, at about upper end of first volution, dorsoventral and lateral diameters 12 mm (estimated) and 16 mm, respectively. Corresponding diameters 18 mm (estimated) and 29 mm, about 80 mm orad. At highest preserved part of specimen dorsoventral and lateral dimensions 25 mm and 40 mm (estimated). Lateral, ventrolateral, and dorsolateral surface of conch crossed by well-defined short, oblique, acutely rounded ribs which become more widely spaced adorally. At about 140 mm below top of phragmocone, where first conch diameters were measured, ribs are about 3 mm apart. They are about 8 mm apart at most orad part of specimen. Ribs at angle of approximately 30° to sutures; ventral extremities directed adapically and dorsal ends adorally.

Sutures closely spaced and approximately transverse but form very weakly defined ventral saddles. They are about 2 mm apart laterally and 4 mm apart ventrally about 140 mm below top of specimen. They increase in adoral spacing up to top of specimen where lateral spacing 5 mm and ventral 7 mm.

DISCUSSION: *Charactocerina goodwini* can be distinguished from other species of the genus by its very tight coiling and small, well-defined ribs. The latter are narrower and more acute than in most species.

The species is named in honor of Mr. G. W. Goodwin, who assisted the writer during the field season of 1951.

Charactocerina leithi sp. nov.
(Pl. 35, fig. 1; Pl. 36, figs. 1a, b)

OCCURRENCE: One specimen (holotype, G.S.C. No. 10522) from Member No. 3 of Chasm Creek Formation, Churchill River: locality 25290

DESCRIPTION: Holotype exceptionally well-preserved conch with much altered shell material. Plaster cast (plastoholotype, G.S.C. No. 10523) has been made of it. Original sectioned in dorsoventral plane, but only few traces of internal structures found preserved.

Conch about 1185 mm long, measured along ventral side: a probable 150 to 170 mm living chamber and remainder phragmocone. Maximum diameter approximately 220 mm. Whorls depressed dorsoventrally, expand uniformly adorally. In transverse outline ventral side of whorl very flatly rounded, whereas curvature of lateral and dorsolateral sides continuous and almost semicircular. Maximum curvature on ventrolateral side. Impressed zone distinct but not deep and covers about two-thirds of ventral surface of preceding whorl. At ventral distance of about 150 mm (approximately 2 volutions) from assumed position of protoconch, dorsoventral diameter 13 mm and corresponding lateral diameter 16 mm. Dorsoventral and lateral measurements were taken every half volution from this last position. In adoral order they are: 22 mm and 30 mm; 28 mm and 40 mm; 42 mm and 57 mm; 53 mm and 70 mm, respectively. About 150 mm adorally from last measurement, *i.e.*, approximately a third of a volution, dorsoventral and lateral diameters 57 mm and 80 mm, respectively. Base of living chamber thought to be here. Chamber too poorly preserved for measurements. There is, however, suggestion of gradual lateral contraction toward aperture. Possible lateral diameter of aperture estimated at 55 mm.

Surface ornamented by fine growth striae about 0.5 mm apart in early growth stages increasing to about 3 mm toward aperture. These striae indicate progressive positions of deep ventral hyponomic sinus and make shallow dorsal "lobes" and very shallow lateral "saddles". Lateral surface of conch ornamented by coarse, rounded transverse ribs slightly convex adorally. Ribs much more pronounced in early growth stages and about 3 mm apart. Adorally they become progressively fainter and increase in spacing to about 25 mm before dying out about $3\frac{1}{2}$ volutions from apex.

Sutures obscured by shell material. Septa concave both dorsoventrally and laterally, and concavity approximately equal to depth of one camera. At second volution septa in center of whorl about 4 mm apart. This distance gradually increases adorally until at fourth volution it is about 15 mm.

Siphuncle cyrtochoanitic, preserved where dorsoventral diameter of conch approximately 53 mm. Center about 12 mm from ventral wall, and at passage through septum diameter 5 mm. Between septa it enlarges to diameter of about 10 mm.

DISCUSSION: *Charactocerina leithi* differs from all previously described species of the genus in having better defined and much coarser ribs. Numerous fragments of this species were seen in Member No. 3, and it would appear that this cephalopod, together with *Antiplectoceras shamattawaense*, and *Huronia septata* are useful guide fossils for this unit.

The species is named in honor of Professor E. I. Leith of the University of Manitoba.

Genus *Wilsonoceras* Foerste, 1929
Type Species: *Trochoceras McCharlesii* Whiteaves, 1889

Miller, Youngquist, and Collinson (1954, p. 111) have recently discussed the nomenclatural history of this genus.

The conch is loosely coiled and in most specimens attains a large size. The phragmocone may be slightly coiled, but the living chamber is typically free. The transverse whorl outline is subelliptical and the lateral diameter is the longer.

Sutures form very shallow lateral saddles and dorsal lobes and rather deep ventral lobes.

According to Miller, Youngquist, and Collinson, the "Siphuncle [is] dorsal but not marginal, and is composed of globular to nummuloidal segments; septal necks [are] rather long."

Wilsonoceras squawcreekense Miller
(Pl. 32, fig. 2)

1900 [?] *Trochoceras* sp. WHITFIELD, American Mus. Nat. Hist., Bull., v. 13, p. 21
1932 *Wilsonoceras squawcreekense* MILLER, Trans. Connecticut Acad. Arts and Sci., v. 31, p. 261, Pl. 19, fig. 1; Pl. 21, figs. 2, 3
1935 *Wilsonoceras bighornense* Miller [*partim*]. FOERSTE, Denison Univ. Bull., Jour. Sci. Lab., v. 30, p. 79, Pl. 16, fig. 1
1954 *Wilsonoceras squawcreekense* Miller. MILLER, YOUNGQUIST, and COLLINSON, Geol. Soc. America Mem. 62, p. 111, Pl. 55, fig. 1

OCCURRENCE: One specimen (hypotype, G.S.C. No. 10537) from Member No. 2 of Portage Chute Formation, Churchill River: locality 25275

DESCRIPTION: Specimen referred to this species poorly preserved, adapically incomplete internal mold which has one of lateral sides missing. Most dorsal and ventral surfaces preserved, however, so that dorsoventral diameters can be determined with fair degree of certainty.

Coiling, rate of enlargement, suture pattern and spacing almost identical with that of holotype illustrated by Miller (1932). Churchill River specimen approximately 1150 mm in length, measured along ventral side, of which about 550 mm assumed living chamber and remainder phragmocone. Specimen probably about 200 mm longer adorally than holotype and enlarges from dorsoventral diameter of 47 mm at adapical end to diameter of 65 mm (estimated) at assumed junction of phragmocone and living chamber. At aperture corresponding diameter is 80 mm.

Sutures form lateral saddles and broad dorsal and ventral lobes, adapically about 16 mm apart on lateral sides, decreasing to about 10 mm near living chamber.

Living chamber of Churchill River specimen seems abnormally long. May be much shorter, since writer places assumed base at uppermost preserved suture.

DISCUSSION: The holotype is from the Lander Sandstone Member of the Bighorn Formation, Wyoming. *Wilsonoceras squawcreekense* has also been found by Miller, Youngquist, and Collinson in the Ordovician of Silliman's Fossil Mount, southern Baffin Island.

Genus *Kinaschukoceras* nov.

Type Species: *Kinaschukoceras churchillense* sp. nov.

DIAGNOSIS: Large, nautiliform cephalopods having whorls more or less laterally compressed in earlier growth stages and an elliptical transverse outline. In later stages the ventral wall becomes markedly concave and is bounded on both sides by a well-defined, acutely ridged ventrolateral keel.

Sutures are approximately transverse on the lateral sides, cross the ventrolateral keels as weakly defined saddles, and form acutely pointed dorsal and ventral lobes.

The siphuncle appears to be suborthochoanitic and tubular in shape.

DISCUSSION: The description of the genus is based on the single species *K. churchillense* sp. nov., which is known from five very poorly preserved specimens. Specimens of *Kinaschukoceras* can be easily recognized by the concave ventral side with the two ventrolateral keels, features so far as known not found in any other Ordovician nautiloid.

The closest genera are thought to be *Fremontoceras* and *Apsidoceras*. The former is very similar to *Kinaschukoceras* in that the sutures form ventral lobes and small ventrolateral saddles. The ventral wall of *Fremontoceras* is flattened, but if it were concave it would be shaped very similarly to that of *Kinaschukoceras*. *Apsidoceras* may, perhaps, be even more closely related than *Fremontoceras*. It is characterized by a flat ventral side, slightly concave along the outer ventral margins in most specimens and in many ridged with a small median-ventral elevation. Most sutures form ventral lobes and small ventrolateral saddles.

The genus is named in honor of Mr. and Mrs. J. Kinaschuk, formerly of Mile 352, Hudson Bay Railway, who greatly assisted the writer in surveying Nelson River during the field season of 1951.

Kinaschukoceras churchillense sp. nov.

(Pl. 37, fig. 3)

OCCURRENCE: Five specimens from Member No. 4 of Chasm Creek Formation, Churchill River: localities 25291, 25292

Holotype, G.S.C. No. 10802⎫
Paratype, G.S.C. No. 10803⎬ locality 25292
Paratype, G.S.C. No. 10804: locality 25291

DESCRIPTION: Species based on five very poorly preserved, dolomitized specimens. Each, alone, would not warrant specific or generic determination. Together, however, they provide fairly accurate picture of species. Holotype consists of about 4½ volutions, but no details such as sutures or internal structures preserved. Paratype 10803 similar to holotype in shape and size. It was sectioned across umbilical area for details of transverse whorl outlines at different growth stages. Paratype No. 10804 portion of phragmocone, 3–4 volutions from apex. It has given information about sutures, septa, and siphuncle at this position.

Conch nautiliform and attains maximum diameter of approximately 280 mm across 5 volutions. Rate of dorsoventral and lateral enlargement gradual and uniform. Up to about third volution, whorls elliptical in transverse outline and dorsoventral diameter is longer. Where ventral depression present, the two diameters nearly equal; lateral slightly longer. Depression appears to form after about third volution and is bounded on both sides by acutely ridged ventrolateral keel. Dorsal impressed zone may be present during introduction of ventral depression. Following measurements were made on paratype No. 10803, but because of preservation are approximate. At second volution, dorsoventral and lateral diameters 18 mm and 10 mm; at third 28 mm and 23 mm; and at fourth 32 mm and 38 mm, respectively. Maximum depth of ventral depression below keels on holotype 5 mm, where lateral diameter 40 mm, and 8–10 mm where this diameter 48 mm.

Sutures form small, apparently acutely angulated dorsal lobes and extend nearly transversely across lateral sides. They obliquely cross keels as poorly defined ventrolateral saddles and apparently form angulated ventral lobes. Depth of these ventral lobes below corresponding saddles equivalent to

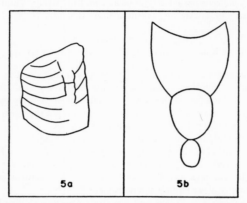

5a   5b

FIGURE 5. *Kinaschukoceras churchillense* sp. nov. Figures 5 a, b reconstructed drawings of paratypes No. 10804 and 10803, respectively, × ½. Figure 5a shows details of septa and siphuncle; 5b the reconstructed transverse whorl outline

length of 1½ camerae. Median parts of ventral and dorsal lobes not preserved, but curvature of sutures toward these centers suggests probable angulated pattern. At estimated dorsoventral and lateral conch diameter of 34 mm and 40 mm, respectively, sutures about 7 mm apart on lateral sides. Concavity of septa at this position equivalent to length of 1½ camerae and maximum curvature closer to ventral than dorsal side.

Siphuncle ventral and its ventral wall, at position where above measurements of sutures and septa were taken, about 5 mm from conch wall. It appears tubular, has very little expansion between septa and has diameter of about 6 mm. Dorsal part of septal neck appears abruptly bent at right angles to septum. Ventral part makes angle of almost 130° with it.

REFERENCES CITED

ALCOCK, F. J., 1916, Lower Churchill River region, Manitoba: Geol. Survey Canada Sum. Rept. 26, p. 133–136

BAILLIE, A. D., 1951, Silurian geology of the Interlake area, Manitoba: Manitoba Dept. Mines Nat. Res. Mines Branch Pub. 50–1, 82 p.

———— 1952, Ordovician geology of Lake Winnipeg and adjacent areas, Manitoba: Manitoba Dept. Mines Nat. Res. Mines Branch Pub. 51–6, 64 p.

BASSLER, R. S., 1950, Faunal lists and descriptions of Paleozoic corals: Geol. Soc. Am. Mem. 44, 315 p.

BELL, ROBERT, 1879, Report on the country between Lake Winnipeg and Hudson's Bay, 1878: Geol. Survey Canada Rept. Prog. 1877–1878, cc 31 p.

———— 1880, Report on explorations on the Churchill and Nelson rivers and around Gods and Island lakes, 1879: Geol. Survey Canada Rept. Prog. 1878–1879, c 44 p.

BILLINGS, E., 1866, Catalogues of the Silurian fossils of the Island of Anticosti, with descriptions of some new genera and species: Geol. Survey Canada, 93 p.

BOLTON, T. E., 1961, Ordovician and Silurian formations of Anticosti Island, Quebec: Geol. Survey Canada Paper 61–26, 18 p.

BUEHLER, E. J., 1955, The morphology and taxonomy of the Halysitidae: Yale Univ., Peabody Mus. Nat. Hist. Bull. 8, 79 p.

BULMAN, O. M. B., 1938, Graptolithina *in* Schindewolf, O. H., Handbuch der Palaozoologie: v. 2D, pt. 2, Berlin, Borntraeger, 92 p.

COX, IAN, 1936, Revision of the genus *Calapoecia* Billings: Natl. Mus. Canada Bull. 80, Geol. Ser. 53, 49 p.

———— 1937, Arctic and some other species of *Streptelasma*: Geol. Mag., v. 74, no. 1, p. 1–19

DOWLING, D. B., 1900, Report on the geology of the west shore and islands of Lake Winnipeg: Geol. Survey Canada Ann. Rept., v. 11, pt. F., 100 p.

DUNCAN, H., 1956, Ordovician and Silurian coral faunas of western United States: U. S. Geol. Survey Bull. 1021-F, p. 209–236

———— 1957, *Bighornia*, a new Ordovician coral: Jour. Paleont., v. 31, no. 3, p. 607–615

ETHERIDGE, R., 1878, Palaeontology of the coasts of the Arctic lands visited by the late British expedition under Captain Sir George Nares, R.N., K.C.B., F.R.S.: Geol. Soc. London Quart. Jour., v. 34, p. 568–639

ETHINGTON, R. and FURNISH, W. M., 1959, Ordovician conodonts from northern Manitoba: Jour. Paleont., v. 33, no. 4, p. 540–546

FLOWER, R. H., 1946, Ordovician cephalopods of the Cincinnati region, Part I: Bull. Am. Paleont., v. 29, no. 116, 656 p.

———— 1952, New Ordovician cephalopods from eastern North America: Jour. Paleont., v. 26, no. 1, p. 24–59

———— 1956, Age of the Red River faunas (Ordovician), Manitoba to New Mexico (Abstract): Geol. Soc. Am. Bull., v. 67, p. 1696

———— 1957, Studies of the Actinoceratida, Part I, The Ordovician development of the Actinoceratida, with notes on Actinoceroid morphology and Ordovician stratigraphy: New Mexico Inst. Mining and Tech. State Bur. Mines Min. Res. Mem. 2, p. 1–59

FLOWER, R. H. and TEICHERT, C., 1957, The cephalopod order Discosorida: Univ. Kansas Pal. Contr., Mollusca, art. 6, 144 p.

FOERSTE, A. F., 1928, Contributions to the geology of Foxe Land, Baffin Island; Part II: The cephalopods of Putnam Highland, Michigan: Univ. Mus. Pal. Contr., v. 3, no. 3, p. 25–70

———— 1929, The cephalopods of the Red River formation of southern Manitoba: Denison Univ. Bull., v. 29, no. 7, (Sci. Lab. Jour. v. 24) p. 129–235

———— 1935, Big Horn and related cephalopods, Denison Univ. Bull.: v. 35, no. 5, (Sci. Lab. Jour., v. 30), p. 1–196

———— 1936, The cephalopods of the Maquoketa shale of Iowa: Denison Univ. Bull., v. 35, no. 17 (Sci. Lab. Jour., v. 30), p. 231–257

FOERSTE, A. F. and COX, IAN, 1936, Cephalopods and a *Beatricea* from Akpatok Island: Geol. Mag., v. 73, no. 7, p. 289–307

FOERSTE, A. F., and SAVAGE, T. E., 1927, Ordovician and Silurian cephalopods of the Hudson Bay area: Denison Univ. Bull., v. 27, no. 3, (Sci. Lab. Jour., v. 22), p. 1–107

HILL, DOROTHY, 1953, The Middle Ordovician of the Oslo region, Norway, part 2. Some rugose and tabulate corals: Norsk Geologisk Tidsskr., v. 31, p. 143–168

HUME, G. S., 1925, The Palaeozoic outlier of Lake Timiskaming, Ontario and Quebec: Geol. Survey Canada Mem. 145, 129 p.

KAY, G. M., 1935, Ordovician Stewartville-Dubuque problems: Jour. Geol., v. 43, no. 6, p. 561–590

KIRK, E., 1925, Notes on an early collection of Paleozoic fossils from Ellesmereland: Am. Jour. Sci., 5th ser., v. 10, p. 445–447

KNIGHT, J. B., 1941, Paleozoic gastropod genotypes: Geol. Soc. Am. Spec. Paper 32, 510 p.

LADD, H. S., 1929, The stratigraphy and paleontology of the Maquoketa shale of Iowa, Part I: Iowa Geol. Survey Ann. Rept., v. 34, p. 305–448

LAMBE, L. M., 1899, A revision of the genera and species of Canadian Palaeozoic corals. The madreporaria perforata and the alcyonaria: Geol. Survey Canada Contr. Can. Palaeont., v. 4, pt. 1, p. 1–96

———— 1901, A revision of the genera and species of Canadian Palaeozoic corals. The madreporaria aporosa and the madreporaria rugosa: Geol. Survey Canada Contr. Can. Palaeont., v. 4, pt. 2, p. 97–197

LEITH, E. I., 1944, *Halysites gracilis* from the Ordovician of Manitoba: Jour. Paleont., v. 18, no. 3, p. 268–270

———— 1952, Schizocoralla from the Ordovician of Manitoba: Jour. Paleont., v. 26, no. 5, p. 789–796

McINNES, W., 1913, The basins of the Nelson and Churchill rivers: Geol. Survey Canada Mem. 30, 146 p.

MILLER, A. K., 1930, The age and correlation of the Bighorn Formation of northwestern United States: Am. Jour. Sci., 5th ser., v. 20, no. 17, p. 195–213

———— 1932, The cephalopods of the Bighorn Formation of the Wind River Mountains of Wyoming: Connecticut Acad. Arts Sci., v. 31, p. 193–297

MILLER, A. K., and CARRIER, J. B., 1942, Ordovician cephalopods from the Bighorn Mountains of Wyoming: Jour. Paleont., v. 16, no. 5, p. 531–548

MILLER, A. K., and FURNISH, W. M., 1937, Ordovician cephalopods from the Black Hills, South Dakota: Jour. Paleont., v. 11, no. 7, p. 535–551

MILLER, A. K., and YOUNGQUIST, W., 1947a, Ordovician fossils from the southwestern part of the Canadian Arctic Archipelago: Jour. Paleont., v. 21, no. 1, p. 1–18

———— 1947b, Ordovician cephalopods from the west-central shore of Hudson Bay: Jour. Paleont., v. 21, no. 5, p. 409–419

MILLER, A. K., YOUNGQUIST, W., and COLLINSON, C., 1954, Ordovician cephalopod fauna of Baffin Island: Geol. Soc. Am. Mem. 62, 234 p.

MILNE-EDWARDS, H. M., and HAIME, J., 1851, Monographie des polypiers fossiles des terrains Palaeozoiques: Mus. Nat. Histoire Natl. Arch., v. 5, 502 p.

———— 1854, A monograph of the British fossil corals, fifth part corals from the Silurian formation: Palaeontographical Soc., p. 245–299

NELSON, S. J., 1953, Ordovician stratigraphy and paleontology of the northern Hudson Bay Lowlands (Abstract): Geol. Soc. Am. Bull., v. 64, p. 1458

———— 1959a, Arctic Ordovician fauna: an equatorial assemblage?: Jour. Alberta Soc. Pet. Geol., v. 7, no. 3, p. 45–47, 53.

———— 1959b, Guide fossils of the Red River and Stony Mountain equivalents (Ordovician): Jour. Alberta Soc. Pet. Geol., v. 7, no. 3, p. 51–61

————1964, Ordovician stratigraphy of northern Hudson Bay Lowland: Geol. Survey Canada Bull. 108 (in press)

NICHOLSON, H. A. and ETHERIDGE, R., 1878, A monograph of the Silurian fossils of the Girvan district in Ayshire: Edinburgh and London, I, fasc. 1, 135 p.

OKULITCH, V. J., 1943, The Stony Mountain Formation of Manitoba: Roy. Soc. Canada Tr., v. 37, sec. 4, p. 59–74

PARKS, W. A., 1910, Ordovician stromatoporoids of America: Toronto Univ. Studies, Geol. Ser. 7, 52 p.

———— 1915, Palaeozoic fossils from a region southwest of Hudson Bay, a description of the fossils collected by Joseph B. Tyrrell, Esq., F.R.S.C., in the District of Patricia, Ontario, and in northern Manitoba during the summer of 1912: Roy. Can. Inst. Tr., v. 11, p. 3–95

PORTER, J. W. and FULLER, J. G. C. M., 1959, Lower Paleozoic rocks of northern Williston basin and adjacent areas: Am. Assoc. Pet. Geol. Bull., v. 43, no. 1, p. 124–189

RADUGUIN, K. V., 1936, Some coelenterates from the Lower Silurian of Gornaya Shoria: Records of the geology of the West-Siberian Region, no. 35, p. 89–106 (West Siberian Geological Trust, Tomsk)

RAYMOND, P. E., 1914, A *Beatricea*-like organism from the Middle Ordovician: Geol. Survey Canada Mus. Bull. 5, Geol. Ser. 21, p. 1–19

ROY, S. K., 1941, The Upper Ordovician fauna of Frobisher Bay, Baffin Land: Field Mus. Nat. Hist. Geol. Mem., v. 2, 212 p.

RUEDEMANN, R., 1947, Graptolites of North America: Geol. Soc. Am. Mem. 19, 652 p.

SAVAGE, T. E., and VAN TUYL, F. M., 1919, Geology and stratigraphy of the area of Paleozoic rocks in the vicinity of Hudson and James Bays: Geol. Soc. Am. Bull., v. 30, p. 339–378

SCHUCHERT, C., 1900, On the Lower Silurian (Trenton) fauna of Baffin Land, U.S. Natl. Mus. Pr., v. 22, p. 143–177

SINCLAIR, G. W., 1955, Some Ordovician halysitoid corals: Roy. Soc. Canada Tr., v. 49, sec. 4, p. 95–103

———— 1956a, Review of "Ordovician Cephalopod fauna of Baffin Island": Am. Jour. Sci., 5th ser., v. 254, no. 2, p. 126–128

———— 1956b, Age of the Ordovician English Head Formation (Abstract): Geol. Soc. Am. Bull., v. 67, no. 12, pt. 2, p. 1734

———— 1959, Succession of Ordovician rocks in southern Manitoba: Geol. Survey Canada Paper 59–5, 9 p.

SINCLAIR, G. W. and BOLTON, T. E., 1956, Notes on halysitid corals: Jour. Paleont., v. 30, no. 1, p. 203–206

SINCLAIR, G. W. and LEITH, E. I., 1958, New name for an Ordovician shale in Manitoba: Jour. Paleont., v. 32, no. 1, p. 243–244

STEARN, C. W., 1953, Ordovician-Silurian boundary in Manitoba (Abstract): Geol. Soc. Am. Bull., v. 64, no. 12, pt. 2, p. 1477

———— 1956, Stratigraphy and palaeontology of the Interlake Group and Stonewall Formation of southern Manitoba: Geol. Survey Canada Mem. 281, 162 p.

SWEET, W. C., 1954, Harding and Fremont formations, Colorado: Bull. Am. Assoc. Pet Geol., v. 38, no. 2, p. 284–305

———— 1955, Cephalopods from the Fremont Formation of central Colorado: Jour. Paleont., v. 29, no. 1, p. 71–82

SWEET, W. C. and MILLER, A. K., 1957, Ordovician cephalopods from Cornwallis and Little Cornwallis Islands, District of Franklin, Northwest Territories: Geol. Survey Canada Bull. 38, 86 p.

TEICHERT, C., 1937, Ordovician and Silurian faunas from Arctic Canada: Fifth Thule Exped. 1921–1924 Rept., v. 1, no. 5, 169 p.

TROEDSSON, G. T., 1926, On the Middle and Upper Ordovician faunas of northern Greenland, I. Cephalopods: Medd. om Grønland, v. 71, 157 p.

———— 1928, On the Middle and Upper Ordovician faunas of northern Greenland, II: Medd. om Grønland, v. 72, 197 p.

TWENHOFEL, W. H., 1928, Geology of Anticosti Island: Geol. Survey Canada Mem. 154, 481 p.

TWENHOFEL, W. H., et al., 1954, Correlation of the Ordovician formations of North America: Geol. Soc. Am. Bull., v. 65, p. 247–298

TYRRELL, J. B., 1913, Hudson Bay exploring expedition, 1912: Ontario Bur. Mines Ann. Rept. 22, pt. 1, p. 161–209

WHITEAVES, J. F., 1895, Systematic list with references, of the fossils of the Hudson River or Cincinnati Formation at Stony Mountain, Manitoba: Geol. Survey Canada Pal. Foss., v. 3, pt. 2, no. 3, p. 111–128

————— 1896, New fossils from the Winnipeg limestones: Canadian Rec. Sci., p. 388–398 (July)

—————1897, The fossils of the Galena-Trenton and Black River formations of Lake Winnipeg and its vicinity: Geol. Survey Canada Pal. Foss., v. 3, pt. 3, p. 129–242

WHITFIELD, R. P., 1900, Observations on and descriptions of Arctic fossils: Am. Mus. Nat. Hist. Bull., v. 13, p. 19–22

WILLIAMS, M. Y., 1948, The geological history of Churchill, Manitoba: Western Miner, v. 21, no. 6, p. 39–42

WILSON, A. E., 1926, An Upper Ordovician fauna from the Rocky Mountains, British Columbia: Geol. Survey Canada Bull. 44, p. 1–34

—————1931, Notes on the Baffinland fossils collected by J. Dewey Soper during 1925 and 1929: Roy. Soc. Canada Tr., v. 25, sec. 4, p. 285–308

—————1938, Gastropods from Akpatok Island, Hudson Strait: Roy. Soc. Canada Tr., v. 32, sec. 4, p. 25–39

—————1948, Miscellaneous classes of fossils, Ottawa Formation, Ottawa-St. Lawrence valley: Geol. Survey Canada Bull. 11, 116 p.

EXPLANATION OF PLATES 4–37

PLATE 4.—*BEATRICEA*

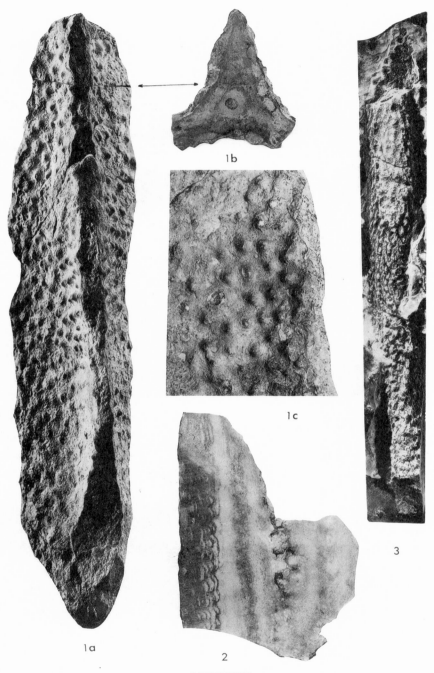

BEATRICEA

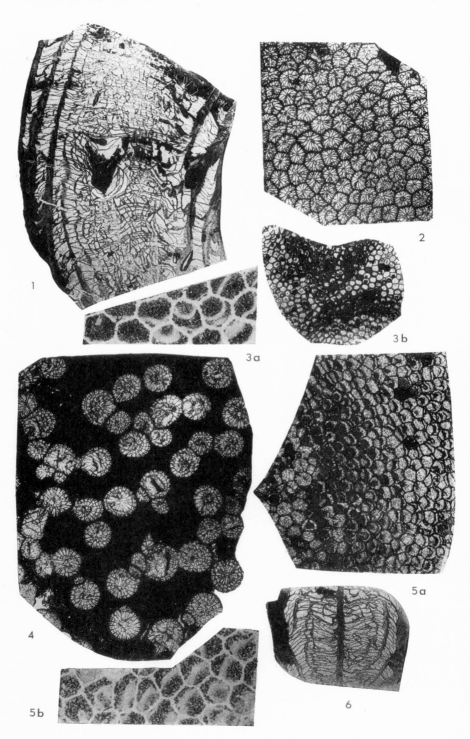

LOBOCORALLIUM, FAVISTELLA, LYOPORA, PALAEOPHYLLUM, AND *BIGHORNIA*

PLATE 5.—*LOBOCORALLIUM, FAVISTELLA, LYOPORA,*
PALAEOPHYLLUM, AND *BIGHORNIA*

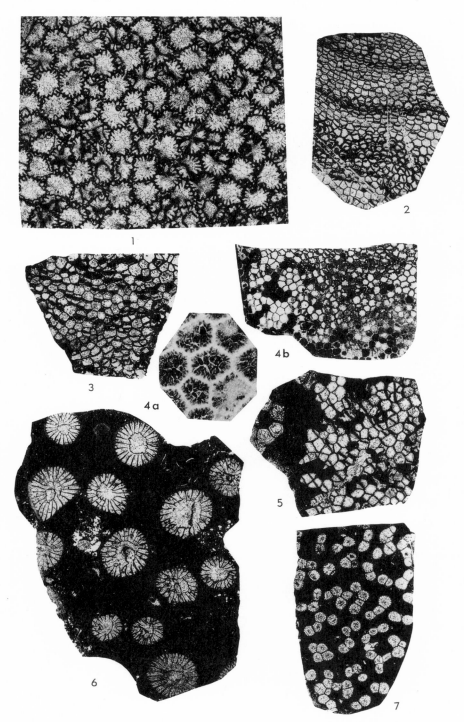

SAFFORDOPHYLLUM(?), *LYOPORA*, *NYCTOPORA*, AND *PALAEOPHYLLUM*

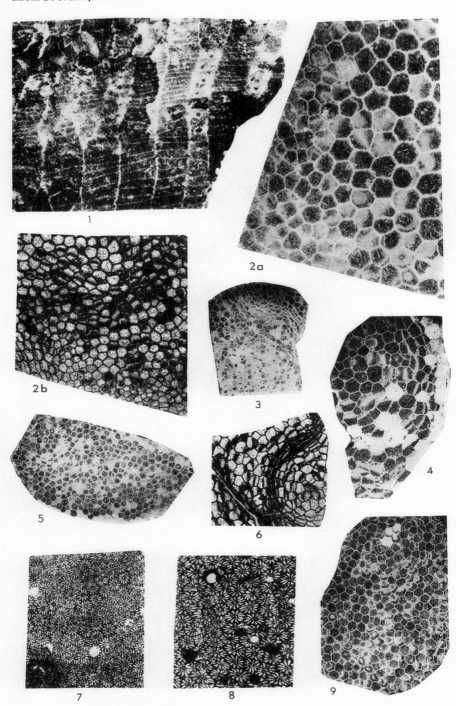

FAVOSITES, PALAEOFAVOSITES, AND *PROTROCHISCOLITHUS*

PLATE 7.—*FAVOSITES, PALAEOFAVOSITES,* AND *PROTROCHISCOLITHUS*

GREWINGKIA, LOBOCORALLIUM, AND *CALAPOECIA*

LOBOCORALLIUM AND *BIGHORNIA*

PLATE 9.—*LOBOCORALLIUM* AND *BIGHORNIA*

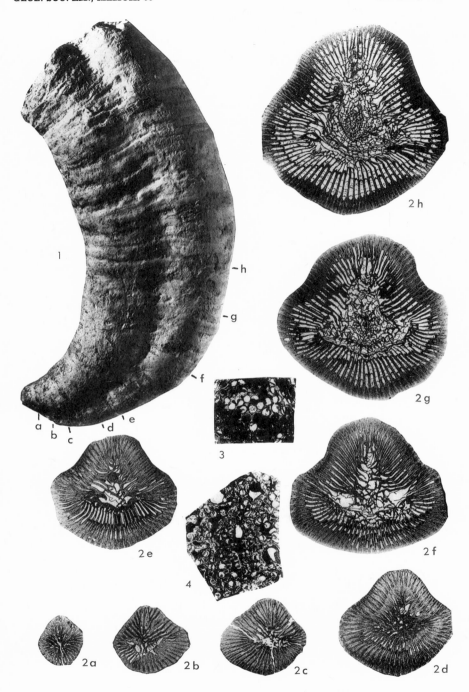

LOBOCORALLIUM AND CALAPOECIA

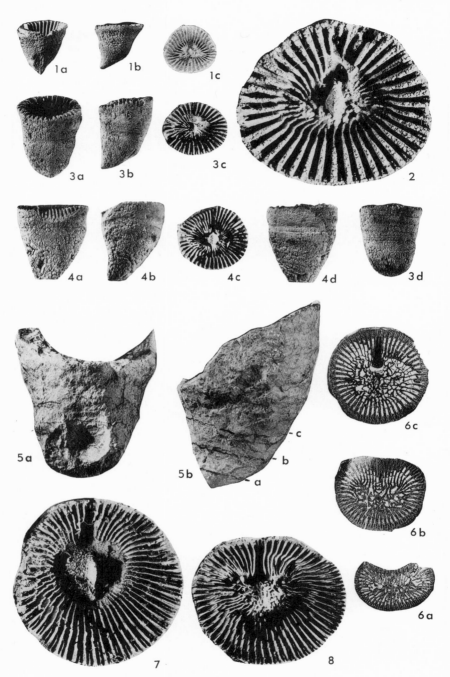

BIGHORNIA

PLATE 11.—*BIGHORNIA*

PLATE 12.—*BIGHORNIA*

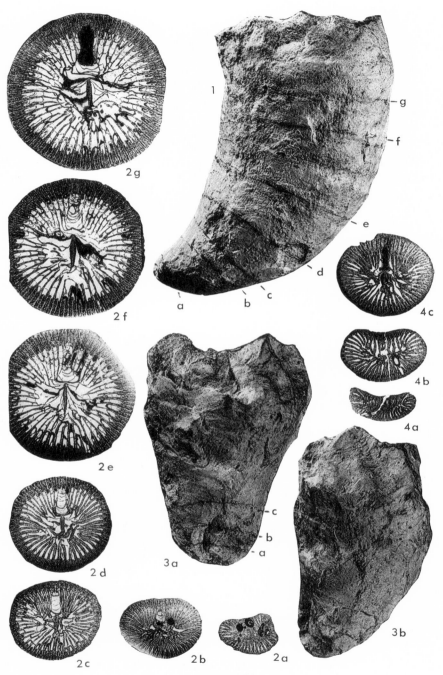

BIGHORNIA

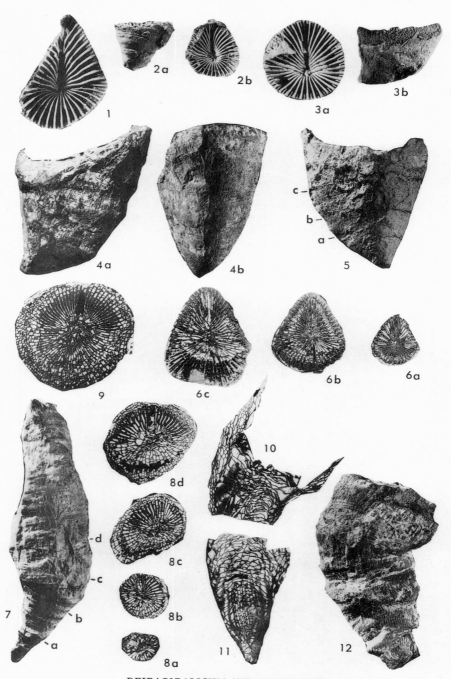

DEIRACORALLIUM AND *PHAULACTIS*

PLATE 13.—*DEIRACORALLIUM* AND *PHAULACTIS*

PLATE 14.—*CATENIPORA* AND *MANIPORA*

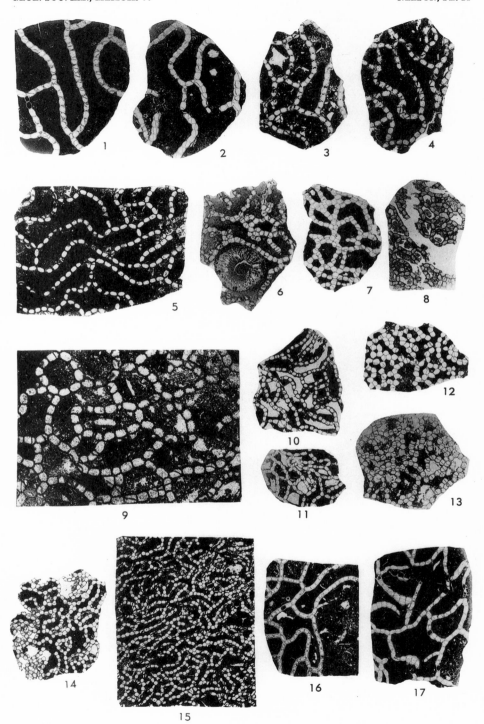

CATENIPORA AND *MANIPORA*

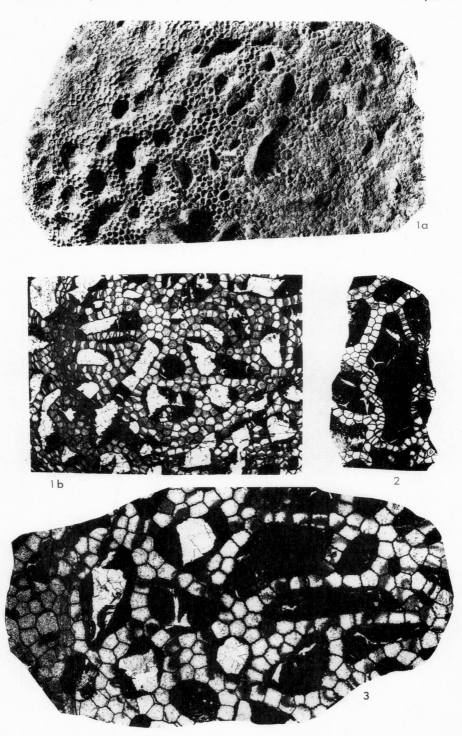

MANIPORA

PLATE 15.—*MANIPORA*

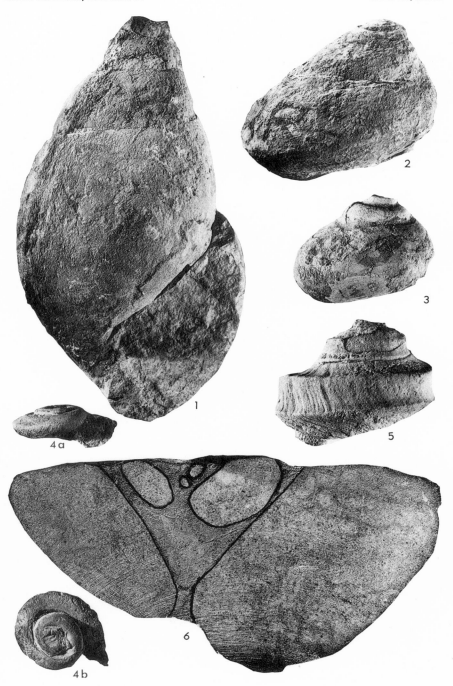

FUSISPIRA, HOLOPEA, LIOSPIRA, TROCHONEMA, AND MACLURITES

CYCLENDOCERAS, FUSISPIRA, AND DESMOGRAPTUS

PLATE 17.—*CYCLENDOCERAS, FUSISPIRA,* AND *DESMOGRAPTUS*

PLATE 18.—*CYCLENDOCERAS* AND *GORBYOCERAS*

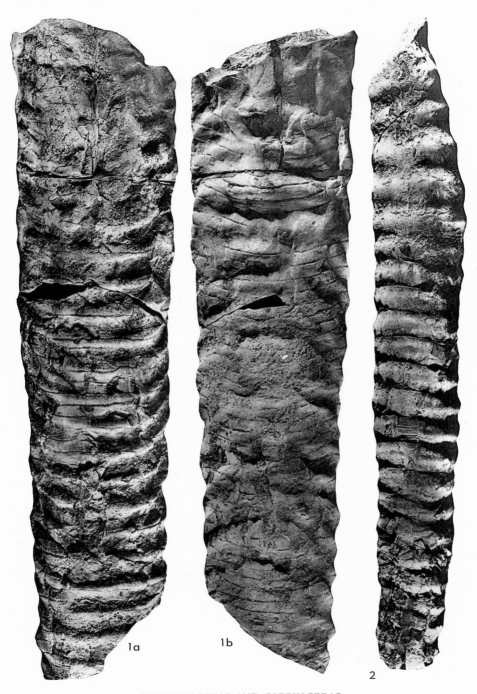

1a   1b   2

CYCLENDOCERAS AND *GORBYOCERAS*

KOCHOCERAS, CHARACTOCERAS, AND *HORMOTOMA*

LAMBEOCERAS, PROBILLINGSITES, AND *PARACTINOCERAS*(?)

DIGENUOCERAS AND *KOCHOCERAS*

PLATE 21.—*DIGENUOCERAS* AND *KOCHOCERAS*

WHITEAVESITES AND BILLINGSITES

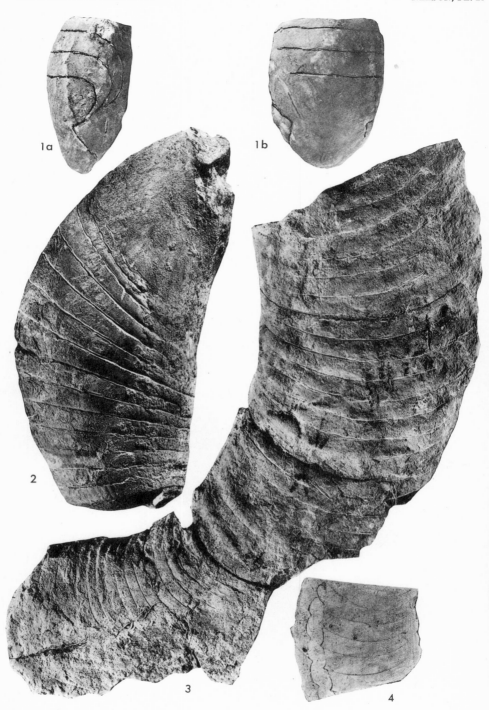

BILLINGSITES, CYRTOGOMPHOCERAS, DIGENUOCERAS, AND WINNIPEGOCERAS

PLATE 23.—*BILLINGSITES, CYRTOGOMPHOCERAS, DIGENUOCERAS,*
AND *WINNIPEGOCERAS*

PLATE 24.—*WINNIPEGOCERAS*

WINNIPEGOCERAS

GORBYOCERAS AND *DIGENUOCERAS*

PLATE 25.—*GORBYOCERAS* AND *DIGENUOCERAS*

1

2

CYRTOGOMPHOCERAS AND *WINNIPEGOCERAS*

CYRTOGOMPHOCERAS AND *WINNIPEGOCERAS*

PLATE 27.—*CYRTOGOMPHOCERAS* AND *WINNIPEGOCERAS*

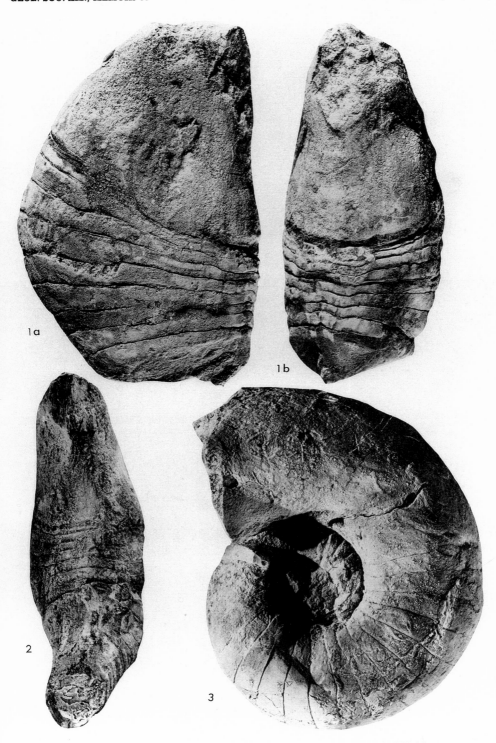

CYRTOGOMPHOCERAS, WINNIPEGOCERAS, AND CHARACTOCERAS

CYRTOGOMPHOCERAS, CHARACTOCERAS, AND PARACTINOCERAS(?)

DIGENUOCERAS, WHITEAVESITES, CHARACTOCERINA, AND *CHARACTOCERAS*

EXOMEGOCERAS, PARKSOCERAS, ANTIPLECTOCERAS, AND WINNIPEGOCERAS

PLATE 31.—*EXOMEGOCERAS, PARKSOCERAS, ANTIPLECTOCERAS,* AND
WINNIPEGOCERAS

LAMBEOCERAS, WILSONOCERAS, WINNIPEGOCERAS, AND *CHARACTOCERINA*

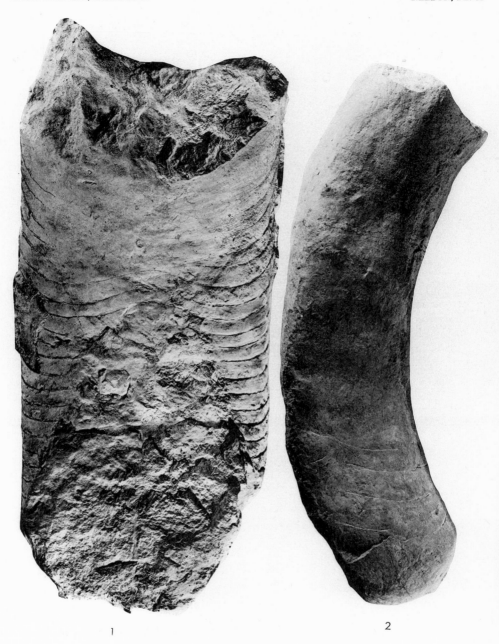

1   2

APSIDOCERAS

PLATE 33.—*APSIDOCERAS*

PLATE 34.—*APSIDOCERAS*

1a

1b

APSIDOCERAS

1

2

CHARACTOCERINA AND *CYRTOGOMPHOCERAS*

PLATE 35.—*CHARACTOCERINA* AND *CYRTOGOMPHOCERAS*

PLATE 36.—*CHARACTOCERINA* AND *NEUMATOCERAS*

CHARACTOCERINA AND NEUMATOCERAS

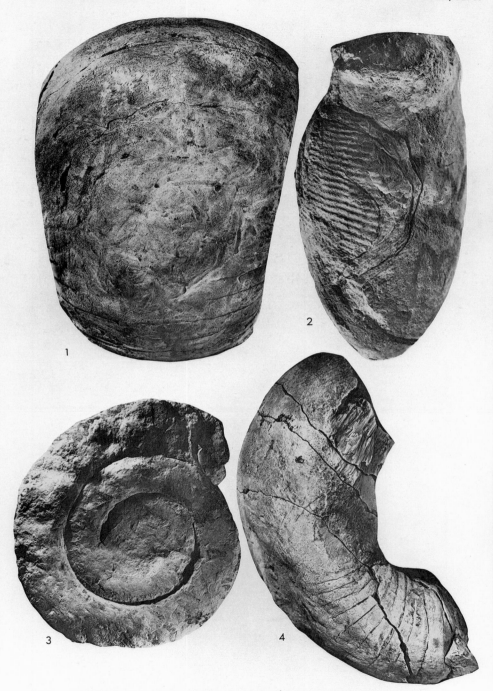

CHARACTOCERAS, BILLINGSITES, AND *KINASCHUKOCERAS*

PLATE 37.—*CHARACTOCERAS, BILLINGSITES* AND *KINASCHUKOCERAS*

INDEX*

---

* Figures in boldface type indicate detailed
descriptions and/or discussions.